DIGITAL TECHNOLOGY
LABORATORY MANUAL

GERALD E. WILLIAMS, P.E.
Riverside City College

SCIENCE RESEARCH ASSOCIATES, INC.
Chicago, Palo Alto, Toronto, Henley-on-Thames, Sydney, Paris, Stuttgart
A Subsidiary of IBM

Library of Congress Cataloging in Publication Data

Williams, Gerald Earl, 1931-
    Digital technology laboratory manual.

    1. Electronic digital computers -- Circuits --
Laboratory manuals. 2. Logic circuits -- Laboratory
manuals. I. Title.
TK7888.4.W54   621.3819'58'2   76-49487
ISBN 0-574-21502-6

Dedication

To my sister Leta

and her family, Mike and Cindy

Acknowledgment.

To Samuel Gerardi

for his careful experimental work

CONTENTS

Introduction

    a. General

    b. Laboratory Reporting

    c. Materials and Equipment Specifications

List of Experiments

INTRODUCTION

This laboratory manual is designed to provide the hands-on experience essential to any real understanding of digital logic. The carefully selected experiments are intended to augment the textbook. Because this manual is designed as a companion to a text, very little theory has been included.

Some guidelines for the important area of laboratory reporting will be given in this introduction. The method mentioned here is widely used in industry but is by no means the only one possible for a given situation. It is, however, representative of scientific reporting methods in general.

Laboratory Reporting

The many methods of reporting data all contain certain common elements. The most common method in industry is the engineering or technologist's notebook. Because this notebook is often used as a legal document in patent cases and the like, it is important to follow certain rules in keeping it. Beyond the legal requirements, it must contain enough easily readable data for you to write a formal technical report from it, perhaps five years or more after you have made the entry in the notebook.

A. Legal requirements

1. Physical construction

   a. The notebook must be hardbound. One example is the Standard B & P (Boorum & Pease) 1602½. This book is ruled in quarter-inch squares for ease in drawing circuits and graphs.

   b. All pages must be machine numbered.

2. Other legal requirements

    a. Each page must be dated and signed.

    b. Ink (felt-tip or ball-point is permissible) must be used for all entries.

    c. No erasures (or ink eradicator) are permitted.

    d. If you make an error, make a single line through the entry. The entry must still be readable after you have lined it through.

    e. Witnesses: Each entry must contain the signature (dated) of at least two witnesses. The witnesses <u>theoretically</u> do not need to understand the nature or meaning of the entry witnessed. They must, however, be able to testify that they are certain that they can identify the entry and that they are certain that they did indeed examine and sign the entry on the date specified.

B. Practical requirements

    1. The report must have a title.

    2. The report must have a stated objective. This is a summary of what you intend to learn from the experiment (or measurements).

    3. The report must include a diagram of the circuit being tested.

    4. The report must include a list of instruments used, including serial numbers. The serial numbers are important because someone may later discover that an instrument involved in your measurements was defective.

    5. All measurement results must be clearly displayed, preferably in some consistent <u>tabular</u> form.

    6. The conclusion is <u>your</u> interpretation of the recorded data and is therefore inherently <u>subjective</u> in nature. The conclusion should <u>not</u> be considered unimportant because of its subjective nature. Your instructor may want to add or substitute other kinds of reporting for those indicated here.

    In an industry setting, the notebook is rarely out of the hands of its keeper, although he or she may be expected to leave it with the employer upon termination. In a classroom setting, however, you will probably be asked to turn in individual experiments for evaluation; therefore you may find it more convenient to keep your reports in a loose-leaf notebook. To give you some idea of what such a notebook should look like, we have included a sample title page and entry page at the end of this manual (Appendix III). Be sure that the reports you turn in contain the information requested on the sample entry page.

Two Important Considerations

1. Always enter data into the notebook <u>immediately</u>. Do not enter measurement results and the like on scraps of paper or in another notebook for entry at a later time. Neatness is important, but not at the expense of immediacy.

2. If special drawings or graphs are to be attached to the notebook, use rubber cement or, if necessary, transparent tape you can write on. In either case, your signature should appear crossing the joint of the insertion and the notebook page. At least two signatures should be used. This practice makes it all but impossible to remove or substitute an insert without leaving evidence of tampering, which is an important consideration from a legal standpoint.

It will be advantageous to you to form good and proper notebook-keeping habits from the beginning. Some employers are quite particular about it.

Some blanks and tables to be filled in are included in this manual to flag important points and to illustrate the proper form for tables and other forms. When you make entries in the laboratory manual, be sure that you record the same information in the technologist's notebook before you leave the laboratory. Entries in the laboratory manual are intended to supplement, not replace, entries in the notebook.

Materials and Equipment Specifications

The following integrated circuits are required for the experiments in this manual. Basing diagrams will be found in the appendix.

7400	Quad Two-Input NAND gate
7402	Quad Two-Input NOR gate
7403	Quad Two-Input NAND gate (open collector)
7404	Hex Inverter
74C04	C-MOS Hex Inverter
7408	Quad Two-Input AND
7410	Triple Three-Input NAND gate
7413	Quad Two-Input Schmitt-Trigger NAND gate
7414	Schmitt Trigger Hex Inverter
7420	Dual Four-Input NAND gate
7432	Quad Two-Input OR gate
7447	Decoder/Driver
7473	Dual J-K Master-Slave Flip-Flop

7474	Dual "D" Edge-Triggered Flip-Flop
7476	Dual J-K Master-Slave Flip-Flop
7481A	(7484A) 16-bit RAM
7486	Quad Two-Input Exclusive-OR gate
7490	Decade Counter
7493	Binary Counter
7495	Left/Right Shift Register
74121	Monostable Multivibrator
74151	Data Selector/Multiplexer
74161	Presettable Counter
74181	Arithmetic/Logic Unit (ALU)
8T04	BCD to Seven-Segment Decoder/Driver
555	Timer

Transistors

2N3393

Diodes

1N914

Display Units

MAN-1
or
MAN-72

Logic Trainer Specifications

The logic trainer for this course should have the following features:

1. One or more debounced pushbuttons

2. Eight indicator lamps with built-in lamp drivers (four are adequate for most experiments)

3. Eight SPDT level switches +5V or GND (four are adequate for most experiments)

4. One clock, TTL compatible, with at least 1 Hz and 1 KHz frequencies available

5. One or more strip-type IC and component sockets (see Appendix I for suppliers and types)

6. One 5V regulated power supply, 1 amp capacity

Some of the less expensive logic trainers on the market have only four indicator lamps and four level switches. They are probably adequate in other respects if they are built around the versatile strip-type socket. Trainers with wired-in gates, usually with gate symbols stenciled on the panel, are probably not suitable for use with this manual.

For those experiments requiring extra level switches or indicators, two trainers can generally be used or outboard extra switches or lamps can be made up.

If you are interested in fabricating extra sections or building complete trainers, the following information can be found in Appendix I.

    a. Socket suppliers

    b. Power supply circuit

    c. Hex lamp driver (LED) circuit

    d. Debounced pushbutton circuit

    e. Clock circuit

    f. Level switch circuit

    g. Logic trainer block diagram

A dual trace triggered sweep oscilloscope is also required for several of the experiments.

CHAPTER ONE

AN INTRODUCTION TO
BASIC LOGIC GATES

In this chapter we will examine the logical properties of basic gates and some combinations of gates. The logical behavior of the individual gates that we will be investigating is quite simple, but these simple gates can be combined in an enormous variety of ways to perform any logical task that might be required.

There are only three basic logic gates, the AND gate, the OR gate, and the inverter. The AND gate and the OR gate can each have any number of inputs but only one output. The inverter has only <u>one</u> input and <u>one</u> output.

We will also examine the NAND gate, which is actually a combination of the AND gate and an inverter. The inverter function is often called the NOT function, and NAND is a contraction of NOT-AND. There is also a NOR (NOT-OR) gate formed in a similar manner. These two combination gates represent the most popular off-the-shelf packages in current use.

We will use three methods to describe the logical properties of gates and combinations of gates: Boolean algebra equations, truth tables, and timing diagrams.

By far the most popular logic circuit in the small-scale integration category is called TTL or T^2L (Transistor-Transistor Logic).

LOGIC FUNCTIONS

There are only three basic logical functions in digital circuits.

1. The AND function, indicated by a dot, an $\times$ sign, or adjacency.
2. The OR operation, indicated by a $+$ sign.
3. The complement (NOT) operation, indicated by a bar over the variable. For example: $\overline{A}$ would be read as NOT A.

1

GATE CONVENTIONS

1. A <u>1</u> on the input of an electronic gate can also
   be designated as <u>high</u>, <u>Hi</u>, <u>H</u>.
2. A <u>0</u> on the input of an electronic gate can also
   be designated as <u>low</u>, <u>Lo</u>, <u>L</u>.
3. A <u>1</u> on the output of an electronic gate can also
   be designated by <u>high</u>, <u>Hi</u> or <u>H</u>, and a <u>0</u> can be
   represented by <u>low</u>, <u>Lo</u> or <u>L</u>. We will follow these
   conventions throughout the book.

When we use indicator lamps to indicate the output state of a gate,
a lit lamp is 1 (Hi) and a dark lamp is 0 (Lo).

All digital circuits are made up of combinations of the electronic
equivalent of simple series and parallel connected switches. The condition
in which switches are mechanically or electronically coupled so that a
certain switch "$\overline{A}$" will <u>always</u> be open when another certain switch "A" is
closed, and switch "$\overline{A}$" will <u>always</u> be closed when switch "A" is open, is
called the complement (NOT, or Negation) function. This operation is performed
by a gate called the Inverter.

TRUTH TABLES

The truth table serves as a concise and complete description of each
output condition for every possible combination of input conditions. Figure
1-1a shows the most popular package style, the dual inline package (DIP).
Figure 1-1b describes the standard logic levels for TTL gates.

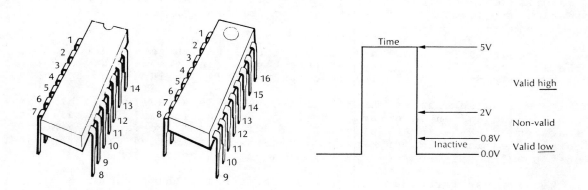

a. Standard DIP package   b. Standard TTL logic levels

Figure 1-1 Standard Integrated Circuit Dual Inline
            Package (DIP) and TTL Logic Levels

In most digital circuits, only two logic levels are allowed to exist.
Within each logic family these levels are carefully defined. In the TTL
family a logic <u>low</u> is defined as any voltage level between 0 and 0.8 volt;
<u>high</u> is +2.0 to +5V. We define logic functions in a form called a <u>truth table</u>.

The AND gate (see Fig. 1-2) produces a logic 1 (<u>high</u>) output only when <u>every</u> input is supplied by a logic 1. For all other input combinations, the output is a logic 0 (<u>low</u>).

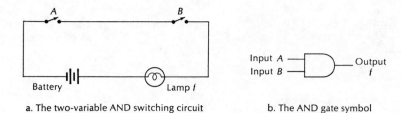

a. The two-variable AND switching circuit

b. The AND gate symbol

c. Equation: $f = (A \cdot B)$

m	Switch A	Switch B	f (lamp)
0	open	open	not lit
1	open	closed	not lit
2	closed	open	not lit
3	closed	closed	lit

d. The two-variable switching-circuit truth table

m	A	B	f
0	0	0	0
1	0	1	0
2	1	0	0
3	1	1	1

$f = (A \cdot B)$

e. The standard truth table

Figure 1-2 AND Circuit, Gate, and Truth Tables

EXPERIMENT 1-1   THE TWO-INPUT AND GATE

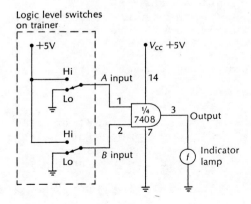

Figure 1-3 Circuit of Experiment 1-1, the AND Gate
(Boolean equation: $f = A \cdot B$)

3

OBJECTIVES:

a. To verify the functional operation of the AND gate.
b. To plot experimental results on a truth table.
c. To read the truth table to determine if experimental results are valid.

MATERIALS:

a. A 7408 integrated circuit, two-input, quad AND gate
b. Miscellaneous interconnecting leads for the logic trainer

EQUIPMENT:

a. Logic trainer (See Appendix I)

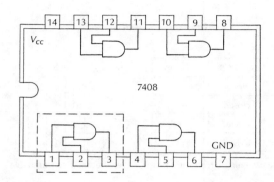

Figure 1-4   Basing Diagram for the 7408 Quad Two-Input AND Gate

PROCEDURE:

a. Connect the 7408 quad AND gate as shown in Figure 1-3. Figure 1-4 shows the basing diagram for the 7408.
b. Connect the inputs of one of the AND gates in the 7408 package to the logic switches (+5V and GND).
c. Connect the output of the AND gate to one of the indicator lamps on the trainer or to a logic probe.
d. Connect V_{CC} to +5V and GND to Ground on the trainer.
e. Proceed through all possible +5/0V conditions for both switches.
f. Record the results on the truth table (Table 1-1b).

GENERAL INFORMATION:

a. The AND gate must have a Hi (+5V) on all inputs for a Hi (+5V) at the output. The AND gate is equivalent to switches in series.
b. No connections are required for an unused gate in the package.
c. Voltages and logic levels for TTL gates are as follows:

4

V_{cc} Power supply voltage, 5.0V ± 10%

V_{ih} High-level input voltage-voltage required for a logic 1 at the input. It is a guaranteed minimum of 2.0V, typically 2.4 to 3.4V.

V_{il} Low-level input voltage-voltage required for logic 0 at an input. It is a guaranteed maximum of 0.8V, typically 0.1 to 0.7V.

V_{oh} High-level output voltage-voltage level output from an output in the logic 1 state. It is a guaranteed minimum of 2.4V.

V_{ol} Low-level output voltage-voltage level output from an output in the logical 0 state. It is a guaranteed maximum of 0.4V.

Note: Indicator lamps must have drivers of some kind to prevent excessive gate loading. Loads of greater than 15mA can cause problems. See Appendix I for lamp driver circuits.

	A	B	f
m_0	Lo	Lo	Lo
m_1	Lo	Hi	Lo
m_2	Hi	Lo	Lo
m_3	Hi	Hi	Hi

	A	B	f
m_0	0	0	0
m_1	0	1	0
m_2	1	0	0
m_3	1	1	1

a. Expected results

$V_{cc} = 5.22$ V

	A	B	f
m_0	Lo	Lo	◯
m_1	Lo	Hi	◯
m_2	Hi	Lo	◯
m_3	Hi	Hi	/

	A	B	f
m_0	0	0	◯
m_1	0	1	◯
m_2	1	0	◯
m_3	1	1	/

high output = 3.91V
low output = .06V

b. Experimental results

Table 1-1   AND Gate Truth Tables

PROBLEMS:

a. Describe in words the operation of the AND gate.

b. How many possible input (+5V,0V) combinations exist for a two-input gate? How many for a three-input gate? *$2^2 = 4$ $2^3 = 8$*

c. The AND gate output will be high only when input *A* is: a. high, or b. low.

d. The typical low input level for a TTL gate is __*.8*__ ?

e. The typical high input level for a TTL gate is__*2.4 to 3.4*__ ?

f. The standard power supply voltage V_{cc} for TTL gates is__*5V*__ ?

g. The highest valid low input voltage for a TTL gate is__*.8V*__ ?

h. The lowest valid high input voltage for a TTL gate is__*2.0V*__ ?

i. The truth table for a three-input AND gate would require how many rows? *8 rows*

EXPERIMENT 1-2 THREE-INPUT AND GATE FORMED FROM A PAIR OF TWO-INPUT AND GATES

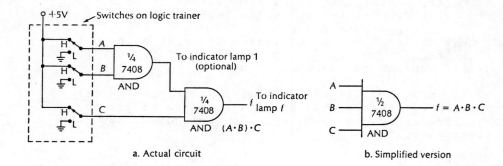

Figure 1-5   Three-Input AND Gate Formed from a Pair of
Two-Input AND Gates (Boolean equation: $f = A \cdot B \cdot C$)

OBJECTIVES:

    a. To construct a three-input AND gate using a pair
of two-input AND gates.

    b. To write a truth table for a three-input AND gate.

    c. To test the three-input AND formed from two two-input
AND gates, complete the functional truth tables for
the circuit, and compare the two sets of truth tables.

MATERIALS:

    a. A 7408 quad two-input AND gate (see Fig. 1-4 for
basing diagram)

    b. Miscellaneous interconnecting leads

EQUIPMENT:

    a. Logic trainer (See Appendix I)

PROCEDURE:

    a. Connect two of the AND gates in the 7408 package as
shown in Figure 1-5.

    b. Follow the combinations on the truth table and set
the logic trainer level switches to each set of conditions on the table (Table 1-2a,b).

    c. Record the results of each setting on the table of
experimental results (Table 1-2a,b).

    d. Compare the two sets of tables.

	4 A	2 B	1 C	f	f_0			4 A	2 B	1 C	f	f_0
m_0	Lo	Lo	Lo	Lo	LO		m_0	0	0	0	0	O
m_1	Lo	Lo	Hi	Lo	LO		m_1	0	0	1	0	O
m_2	Lo	Hi	Lo	Lo	LO		m_2	0	1	0	0	O
m_3	Lo	Hi	Hi	Lo	LO		m_3	0	1	1	0	O
m_4	Hi	Lo	Lo	Lo	LO		m_4	1	0	0	0	O
m_5	Hi	Lo	Hi	Lo	LO		m_5	1	0	1	0	O
m_6	Hi	Hi	Lo	Lo	LO		m_6	1	1	0	0	O
m_7	Hi	Hi	Hi	Hi	H		m_7	1	1	1	1	l

a. Voltage level form   b. Boolean form

Table 1-2 Truth Tables for the Three-Input AND Gate
(f = expected results; f_0 = experimental results)

PROBLEMS:

 a. Define in words the operation of the three-input AND gate.
 b. Find the type numbers for a four-input, five-input, and six-input AND gate in the manufacturer's data book.
 c. Under what circumstances might it be necessary to use several gates to take the place of a single multi-input gate?
 d. Draw a logic circuit showing how a four-input AND gate can be formed using a 7408 package.

EXPERIMENT 1-3 THE TWO-INPUT OR GATE

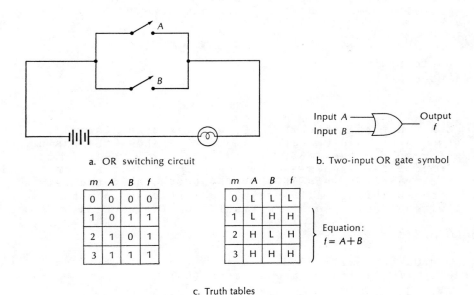

a. OR switching circuit   b. Two-input OR gate symbol

m	A	B	f		m	A	B	f
0	0	0	0		0	L	L	L
1	0	1	1		1	L	H	H
2	1	0	1		2	H	L	H
3	1	1	1		3	H	H	H

Equation:
$f = A + B$

c. Truth tables

Figure 1-6 The OR Function

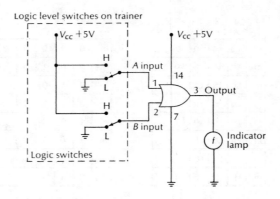

Figure 1-7 Circuit for Evaluating the OR Gate
(Boolean equation: $f = A+B$, read $f = A$ OR B)

The OR operation is equivalent to switches (mechanical or electronic) wired in parallel. Figure 1-6 shows the circuit, symbol, and truth tables for the OR gate.

The following is a summary of what the truth tables say:

a. A 1 (Hi) on <u>any</u> input to the OR gate will yield a 1 output.
b. For a zero output, <u>all</u> inputs must be zero.

OBJECTIVE:

a. To verify that the real OR gate fits the OR truth tables.

MATERIALS:

a. A 7432 quad two-input OR gate
b. Miscellaneous leads for interconnections

EQUIPMENT:

a. Logic trainer
b. Logic probe (optional)

PROCEDURE:

a. Construct the circuit in Figure 1-7 using the 7432 two-input quad OR gate. Figure 1-8 shows the basing diagram for the 7432.
b. Connect the inputs to the logic level switches on the trainer. Connect the output to one of the lamps.
c. Proceed through all possible conditions for both switches and record the results on Tables 1-3a and b.

GENERAL INFORMATION:

a. The OR gate will produce a zero (Lo) output if and only if all inputs are at zero (Lo).

b. "If and only if" is often abbreviated as <u>iff</u>.

8

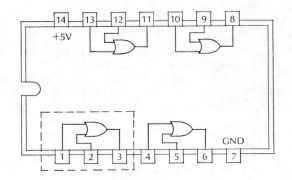

Figure 1-8   Basing Diagram for the 7432 Quad Two-Input OR Gate

m	A	B	f	f_0
0	Lo	Lo	Lo	0
1	Lo	Hi	Hi	1
2	Hi	Lo	Hi	1
3	Hi	Hi	Hi	1

a. Voltage level form

m	A	B	f	f_0
0	0	0	0	0
1	0	1	1	1
2	1	0	1	1
3	1	1	1	1

b. Boolean form

Table 1-3   Two-Input OR Gate Truth Table
(f = expected results; f_0 = experimental results)

PROBLEMS:

    a. Describe the OR gate in words.
    b   Write the equation for a three-input OR gate.
    c. Explain how the OR function differs from the
       AND function.
    d. Provide some examples from daily life of the
       OR and AND concepts.

EXPERIMENT 1-4   CONSTRUCTING A FOUR-INPUT OR GATE USING THREE TWO-INPUT OR GATES

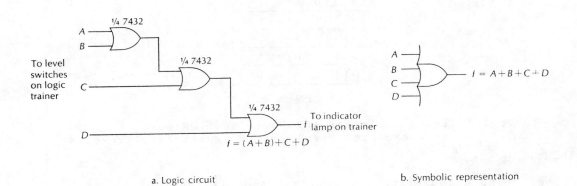

a. Logic circuit

b. Symbolic representation

Figure 1-9   Four-Input OR Gate Composed of Three Two-Input
OR Gates (Boolean equation: $f = A + B + C + D$)

9

OBJECTIVES:

    a.   To construct a four-input OR gate using 3/4 of a quad (4) two-input OR gate package.

    b.   To compare the truth table for the "constructed" OR gate function with the function performed by any four-input OR gate, as defined by the truth table.

MATERIALS:

    a.   A 7432 quad two-input OR gate package

EQUIPMENT:

    a.   Logic trainer

PROCEDURE:

    a.   Construct the circuit as shown in Figure 1-9. See Figure 1-8 for the basing diagram for the 7432.

    b.   Follow the truth table (Table 1-4).

    c.   Set the level switches on the trainer to each combination shown on the truth table and record the results of each combination in f_0 column of the table.

| | 8 | 4 | 2 | 1 | | |
m	A	B	C	D	f	f_0
0	0	0	0	0	0	0
1	0	0	0	1	1	1
2	0	0	1	0	1	1
3	0	0	1	1	1	1
4	0	1	0	0	1	1
5	0	1	0	1	1	1
6	0	1	1	0	1	1
7	0	1	1	1	1	1
8	1	0	0	0	1	1
9	1	0	0	1	1	1
10	1	0	1	0	1	1
11	1	0	1	1	1	1
12	1	1	0	0	1	1
13	1	1	0	1	1	1
14	1	1	1	0	1	1
15	1	1	1	1	1	1

Four variable truth table

Table 1-4   Truth Table for the Four-Input OR Gate
(f = expected results; f_0 = experimental results)

PROBLEMS:

    a.   Find a four-input, five-input, and six-input OR gate in the manufacturer's data manual.

    b.   Draw the logic diagram showing how a five-input OR gate can be implemented using two-input OR gates.

10

EXPERIMENT 1-5   THE INVERTER

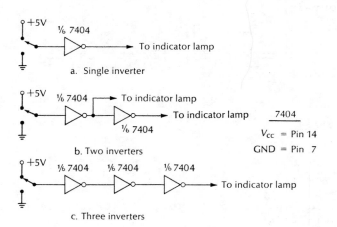

Figure 1-10   Inverter Circuits for Experiment 1-5

The inverter is the simplest of the logic gates, but it is no less valuable than its more complex family members. The inverter is a "black box" that performs the following operations:

a. If $A = 1$, an inverter will convert it to a 0.
b. If $A = 0$, an inverter will convert it to a 1.
c. If A goes in, $\overline{A}$ comes out.
d. If $\overline{A}$ goes in, A comes out.

The following experiments will help you examine and understand the nature of inverters and some of their applications. The inverter performs the complement (NOT) function.

OBJECTIVE:

a. To be able to demonstrate inverter behavior.

MATERIALS:

a. A 7404 hex inverter
b. Miscellaneous interconnecting leads

EQUIPMENT:

a. Logic trainer
b. Logic probe (optional)

11

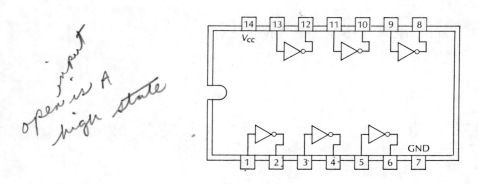

Figure 1-11 Basing Diagram for the 7404 Hex Inverter

PROCEDURE:

a. Using the 7404 hex inverter, construct the circuit
    shown in Figure 1-10a.
b. Connect the input of the inverter to a logic level
    switch and the output to a lamp on the trainer.
c. Proceed through all possible conditions.
d. Record the results in the truth table for a single
    inverter.
e. Follow the same procedure for Figure 1-10b and c
    and record the results for each circuit on the truth
    table (Table 1-5). Figure 1-11 shows the basing
    diagram for the 7404 hex inverter.

#	A	f_1
0	0	1
1	1	0

#	A	f_1	f_2
0	0	1	0
1	1	0	1

#	A	f_1	f_2	f_3
0	0	1	0	1
1	1	0	1	0

a. Single inverter   b. Two inverters   c. Three inverters

Table 1-5 Inverter Truth Table for Experiment 1-5

PROBLEMS:

Complete the following:

a. A 1 input will yield a ___1___ output when "passed
    through" an even number of inverters.
b. A 1 input will yield a ___0___ output when "passed
    through" an odd number of inverters.

12

EXPERIMENT 1-6   TIMING DIAGRAMS FOR AND AND OR GATES

J = K = 1
Every time the clock input goes low,
output changes state

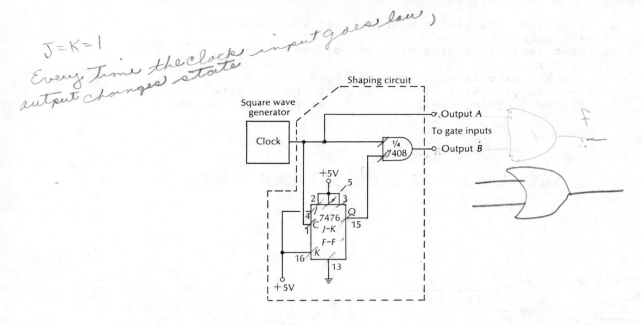

Figure 1-12   Pulse Width Shaping Circuit for Experiment 1-6

OBJECTIVES:

a.   To plot the timing diagram for the two-input
     AND gate.
b.   To plot the timing diagram for the two-input
     OR gate.

MATERIALS:

a.   A 7432 quad two-input OR gate   *7476 will me*
b.   A 7408 quad two-input AND gate
c.   A 7473 J-K master-slave flip-flop
d.   Miscellaneous interconnecting leads
e.   Oscilloscope cables

EQUIPMENT:

a.   Logic trainer
b.   Triggered sweep oscilloscope, dual trace
     preferred

PROCEDURE:

a.   Connect the pulse with the shaping circuit
     as shown in Figure 1-12.
b.   Connect the output *A* of the shaping circuit
     to one input of the 7408 AND gate, and output *B*
     to the second input. Connect the gate output *f*
     to the vertical input of the oscilloscope.
c.   Plot the waveform of the gate on the graph paper.
d.   Replace the AND gate with the 7432 OR gate and
     repeat the procedure. Plot the gate output on
     graph paper.

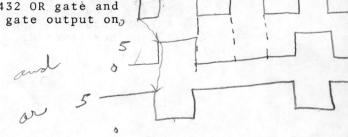

and

or

13

PROBLEMS:

    a.   What does the timing diagram tell you about the
        AND gate?
    b.   What does the timing diagram for the OR gate
        tell you?
    c.   The AND gate is sometimes referred to as a
        coincidence gate. After examining the AND gate
        timing diagram, explain what is meant by this term.

EXPERIMENT 1-7   VERIFYING DE MORGAN'S THEOREM

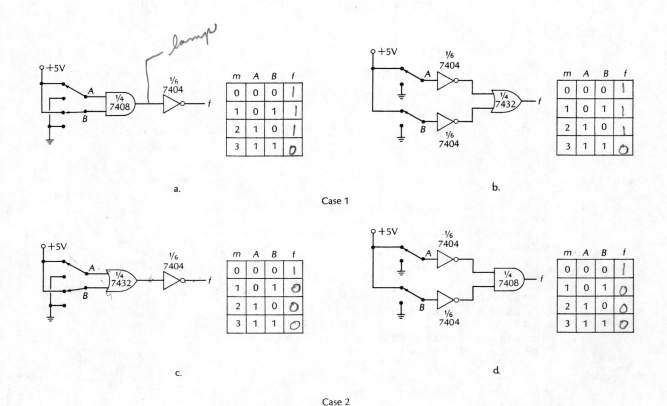

Figure 1-13 De Morgan's Theorem

OBJECTIVES:

    a.   To verify De Morgan's theorem case 1, experimentally.
    b.   To verify De Morgan's theorem case 2, experimentally.

MATERIALS:

    a.   A 7432 quad two-input OR gate
    b.   A 7408 quad two-input AND gate
    c.   A 7404 hex inverter

14

EQUIPMENT:

    a. Logic trainer

PROCEDURE:

    a. Connect the circuit in Figure 1-13a on the logic trainer. Set the logic level switches on the trainer to each condition on the truth table. Complete the f column.

    b. Connect the circuit in Figure 1-13b on the logic trainer and complete the f columns of the truth tables, and compare a and b.

    c. Connect the circuits in Figure 1-13c on the logic trainer and complete the truth table.

    d. Connect the circuits in Figure 1-13d on the logic trainer, complete the truth table, and compare tables c and d.

PROBLEMS:

    a. What does a comparison of truth tables (Figure 1-13a and b) indicate?

    b. What does a comparison of the tables in Figure 1-13c and d prove?

EXPERIMENTS 1-8 AND 1-9   NAND AND NOR LOGIC GATES AND THEIR AND-OR-NOT EQUIVALENTS

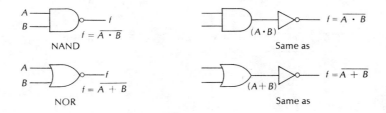

Figure 1-14 NOR and NAND Gate Circuits and Equivalents

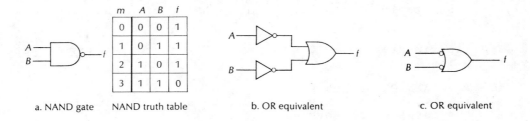

Figure 1-15 NAND-OR Equivalents

15

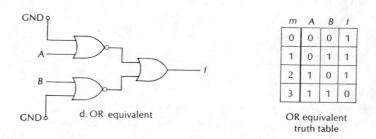

m	A	B	f
0	0	0	1
1	0	1	1
2	1	0	1
3	1	1	0

d. OR equivalent

OR equivalent
truth table

Figure 1-15 (continued)

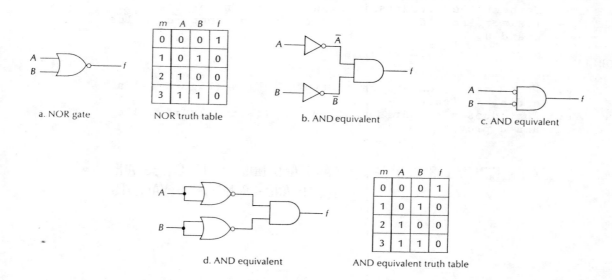

m	A	B	f
0	0	0	1
1	0	1	0
2	1	0	0
3	1	1	0

a. NOR gate   NOR truth table   b. AND equivalent   c. AND equivalent

m	A	B	f
0	0	0	1
1	0	1	0
2	1	0	0
3	1	1	0

d. AND equivalent   AND equivalent truth table

Figure 1-16   The NOR Gate and Its Equivalent Circuits

Most practical gates contain a <u>built-in</u> inverting amplifier, making them into a NOT-AND (NAND) gate and a NOT-OR (NOR) gate. Any logic circuit can be constructed using only NAND gates or only NOR gates. Inverters are provided in nearly all logic circuit families as a matter of convenience although they are not essential from a logic standpoint. Because the NAND and NOR gates have an inverting amplifier as part of their internal struc-ture, they can be used to perform the inverter function. The NAND and NOR gate symbols and their more obvious AND-OR-NOT equivalents are shown in Fig-ure 1-14.

The experiment here will be concerned with four cases of gate circuit equivalent pairs:

a.   The NAND-OR equivalent
b.   The NOR-AND equivalent (These two are based on the two cases of De Morgan's theorem.)
c.   The AND-NOR equivalent
d.   The OR-NAND equivalent (These two are the result of an inversion of both cases of De Morgan's theorem.)

16

Because the previous experiment verified the first two equivalents, we will simply summarize those results (see Figures 1-15 and 1-16) and concentrate on the inverted forms (c and d).

Figures 1-15 and 1-16 summarize cases 1 and 2 of De Morgan's theorem in terms of NAND and NOR equivalent gate structures.

OBJECTIVES:

    a. To discover the functional behavior of the NAND and NOR gate.
    b. To test the AND-NOR and OR-NAND equivalent circuits to determine their function.
    c. To plot equivalent circuit functions on a truth table and compare them to their respective equivalents.

MATERIALS:

    a. A 7408 quad two-input AND gate
    b. A 7432 quad two-input OR gate
    c. A 7404 hex inverter
    d. A 7400 quad two-input NAND gate
    e. A 7402 quad two-input NOR gate

EQUIPMENT:

    a. Logic trainer

PROCEDURE:

Part I: The AND Gate

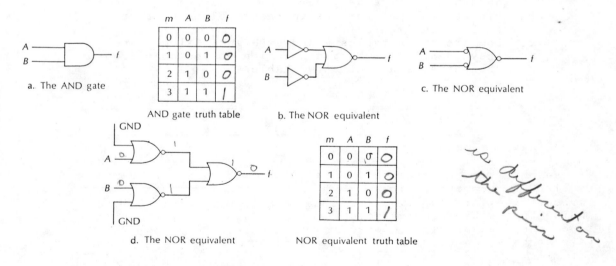

Figure 1-17   AND Gate Equivalents

    a. Given Figure 1-17, connect the AND gate (shown in part a) on the logic trainer. Figure 1-18 shows the basing diagrams for the 7400 and 7402 IC gates.

17

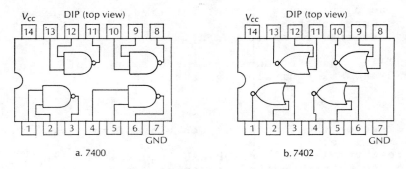

Figure 1-18   Basing Diagrams

b. Connect the inputs on the AND (7408) gate to logic
    level switches on the trainer.
c. Connect the output *f* of the gate to an indicator
    lamp on the trainer.
d. Follow the truth table through, setting each of the
    two logic level switches according to the truth
    table.
e. Plot the output results in the *f* column of truth
    table a in Figure 1-17.

Part II: The NOR Equivalent Circuit

a. Given Figure 1-17, connect the circuit as shown in
    part d. We will be using two gates in the 7402
    quad NOR package as inverters.
b. Plot the output results in the *f* column of truth
    table d in Figure 1-17.
c. Compare truth tables a and d (Figure 1-17). Are
    they identical? What conclusion do you draw from
    the comparison of the two tables?

_____

_____

_____

_____

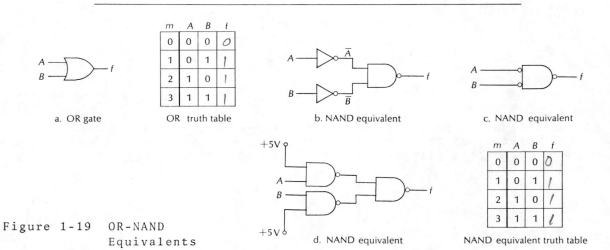

Figure 1-19   OR-NAND
              Equivalents

18

Part III: The OR Gate

a. Given Figure 1-19, complete OR gate truth table a.

Part IV: The NAND Equivalent

a. Given Figure 1-19, connect the circuit as shown in d.
b. Proceed through the various input combinations on the truth table (d) and record the results in the *f* column of the table.
c. Compare tables a and d (Figure 1-19). Are they identical? What conclusion do you draw from a comparison of the two tables?

____

____

____

____

Figure 1-20 summarizes the four equivalent pairs of circuits.

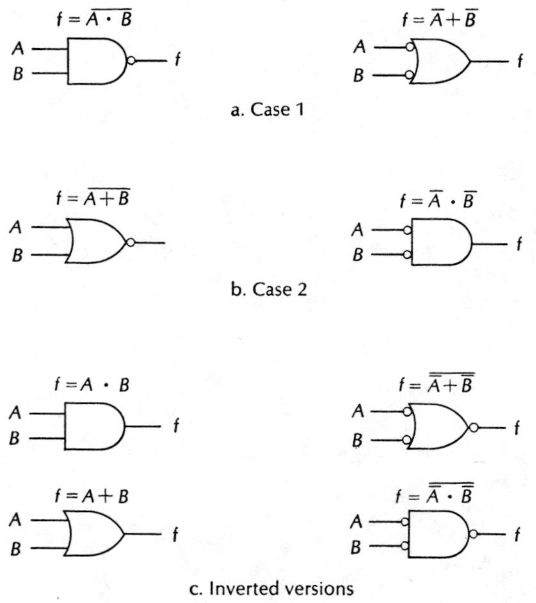
$f = \overline{A \cdot B}$
$f = \overline{A} + \overline{B}$
a. Case 1
$f = \overline{A + B}$
$f = \overline{A} \cdot \overline{B}$
b. Case 2
$f = A \cdot B$
$f = \overline{\overline{A} + \overline{B}}$
$f = A + B$
$f = \overline{\overline{A} \cdot \overline{B}}$
c. Inverted versions

Note: Circles on inputs denote inverters.

Figure 1-20 Summary of DeMorgan's Theorem Gate Equivalents

CHAPTER TWO

USING MANUFACTURER

DATA MANUALS

EXPERIMENT 2-1   DISCOVERING THE DEFINITION OF BASIC PARAMETERS

PROCEDURE:

a. Using the Texas Instruments Data Manual, find the definition of the following parameters:

1. V_{ih} _____

2. V_{il} _____

3. I_{oh} _____

4. V_{ol} _____

5. I_{ih} _____

6. I_{il} _____

7. V_{cc} _____

8. I_{ccl} _____

9. I_{cch} _____

10. T_{plh} _____

11. T_{phl} _____

12. I_{oh} _____

13. V_{oh} _____

b. Using the Signetics Data Manual, find the definition of the following parameters:

1. $V_{in}(1)$ _____

2. $V_{in}(0)$ _____

3. $V_{out}(1)$ _____

4. $V_{out}(0)$ _____

5. $I_{in}(0)$ _____

6. $I_{in}(1)$ _____

7. I_{os} _____

8. V_{cc} _____

9. I_{cc} _____

10. $T_{pd}(0)$ _____

11. $T_{pd}(1)$ _____

PROBLEMS:

a. Match the following:

1. $V_{in}(1)$ _____

2. $V_{in}(0)$ _____

3. $V_{out}(1)$ _____

4. $V_{out}(0)$ _____

5. $I_{in}(1)$ _____

6. $I_{in}(0)$ _____

7. V_{cc} _____

8. I_{cc} _____

9. $T_{pd}(0)$ _____

10. $T_{pd}(1)$ _____

11. I_{os} _____

b. Place in appropriate blank:

(a) V_{cc}

(b) I_{cc_l}

(c) I_{cc_h}

(d) T_{plh}

(e) T_{phl}

(f) I_{il}

(g) V_{ol}

(h) I_{oh}

(i) V_{oh}

(j) I_{ol}

(k) V_{ih}

(l) V_{il}

EXPERIMENT 2-2   FINDING THE VALUE OF BASIC PARAMETERS
USING THE DATA BOOK

PROCEDURE:

Find the values for the following parameters for the 7400, which is considered to be the reference gate for the TTL standard family.

	Parameter	Value
1.	$V_{in}(1)$	_____
2.	$V_{in}(0)$	_____
3.	$V_{out}(1)$	_____
4.	$V_{out}(0)$	_____
5.	$I_{in}(0)$	_____
6.	$I_{in}(1)$	_____
7.	I_{os}	_____
8.	V_{cc}	_____
9.	I_{cc}	_____
10.	$T_{pd}(0)$	_____
11.	$T_{pd}(1)$	_____

PROBLEM:

Given the drawing in Figure 1-1, mark the waveform at appropriate amplitudes, using the symbols from experiment 2-1.

EXPERIMENT 2-3   CASE STYLES AND MECHANICAL DETAILS

PROCEDURE:

a. Using the data book, find the following information:

Package Type

		A	B	f	IN
1.	Number of pins	_____	_____	_____	_____
2.	Pin arrangement	_____	_____	_____	_____
3.	Spacing between pins	_____	_____	_____	_____
4.	Length (or diameter) of package	_____	_____	_____	_____
5.	Width	_____	_____	_____	_____
6.	Package material	_____	_____	_____	_____

b. Describe the L package.

PROBLEMS:

a. What is an 82526? _____

b. What data book(s) did you find it in? _____

c. What is a 74504? _____

d. What data book(s) did you find it listed in? _____

_____

CHAPTER THREE

ASYNCHRONOUS LOGIC

This group of experiments will involve truth tables and equations and the hardware required to implement them. We will examine both gate-only logic and data selector logic. Some practice in simplification will also be involved.

CONSTRUCTING THE TRUTH TABLE

To begin with we need to know how many columns and how many rows to use for the table.

NUMBER OF COLUMNS

    a.   One m column. This simply numbers all of the possible terms in a Boolean equation in X variables.

    b.   One column for each variable in the equation.

        1. $f = (A \cdot B) + (\overline{A} \cdot B) + (\overline{A} \cdot \overline{B})$
            Two variables: A, B

        2. $f = (A \cdot \overline{B} \cdot \overline{C} \cdot \overline{D}) + (\overline{A} \cdot \overline{B} \cdot C \cdot D)$
            Four variables: A, B, C, D

        3. $f = (A \cdot B) + (A \cdot C) + (B \cdot C)$
            Three variables: A, B, C

        4. $f = (\overline{A} \cdot C \cdot \overline{D}) + (B \cdot \overline{C} \cdot D)$
            Four variables: A, B, C, D

    c.   One or more f function columns as needed (generally two or more).

CONSTRUCTING THE UNIVERSAL TRUTH TABLE

Before we start the first experiment, it is important to understand and be able to construct the universal truth table. When completed, this table is a concise description of what the circuit being evaluated is supposed to do. When we check the circuit out in the lab, we enter the output conditions of the circuit under test for each set of input conditions listed on the truth table. There will be two function (f) columns on the table; one of them will state the desired operating behavior of the circuit, while the other will contain the actual performance of the real circuit under test. If the two (f) columns are identical when the test is finished, you can be certain that the circuit is correct for the job and is working properly.

NUMBER OF ROWS

The number of rows is equal to 2^N where 2 is a constant and N is the number of variables. The partially completed three-variable truth table is shown in Table 3-1a.

	4	2	1		
	A	B	C	f	f_0
m_0					
m_1					
m_2					
m_3					
m_4					
m_5					
m_6					
m_7					

a. Partially completed table

	4	2	1		
	A	B	C	f	f_0
m_0	0	0	0		
m_1	0	0	1		
m_2	0	1	0		
m_3	0	1	1		
m_4	1	0	0		
m_5	1	0	1		
m_6	1	1	0		
m_7	1	1	1		

b. Finished table

Table 3-1   The Universal Truth Table

Now to complete the table we write the binary number system column headings in ascending order from right to left as shown in the box above the variables (A, B, C). The headings will be powers of 2: 1 (2^0), 2, 4, 8, and so forth. To finish the table as it appears in part b, we start with row m_0 (we always start numbering the m column with zero because it is possible for all gate inputs to be <u>low</u> - zeros). We write the binary equivalent of decimal zero in three bits (there are three columns). Follow the example and compare it with the entries in Table 3-1b.

	(A) 4	(B) 2	(C) 1			
m_0	0	0	0	=	(0x4) + (0x2) + (0x1)	= 0
m_1	0	0	1	=	(0x4) + (0x2) + (1x1)	= 1
m_2	0	1	0	=	(0x4) + (1x2) + (0x1)	= 2
m_3	0	1	1	=	(0x4) + (1x2) + (1x1)	= 3
m_4	1	0	0	=	(1x4) + (0x2) + (0x1)	= 4
m_5	1	0	1	=	(1x4) + (0x2) + (1x1)	= 5
m_6	1	1	0	=	(1x4) + (1x2) + (0x1)	= 6
m_7	1	1	1	=	(1x4) + (1x2) + (1x1)	= 7

THE EXCLUSIVE-OR AND EXCLUSIVE-NOR CIRCUITS

One particular circuit is so frequently encountered in digital circuits that it has been given a special title and symbols. It is often called
a <u>gate</u>, even though it is not a basic Boolean gate, but a composite of ordinary Boolean gates (see Figure 3-1). We will use this circuit to illustrate
the relationship among truth tables, Boolean equations, and logic diagrams.
Table 3-2 compares the ordinary inclusive-OR and the exclusive-OR. The difference in the two truth tables is significant, though seemingly minor.

$f = A \oplus B$

a. Boolean symbol   b. Logic symbol

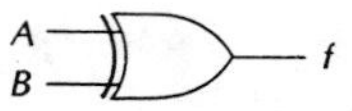

Figure 3-1   The Exclusive-OR Symbols

	A	B	f
m_0	0	0	0
m_1	0	1	1
m_2	1	0	1
m_3	1	1	1

	A	B	f
m_0	0	0	0
m_1	0	1	1
m_2	1	0	1
m_3	1	1	0

Table 3-2   Comparing the Inclusive-OR and
Exclusive-OR Truth Tables

EXPERIMENT 3-1   THE EXCLUSIVE-OR CIRCUIT

OBJECTIVES:

 a. To write the minterm equation from the truth table.
 b. To complement the minterm equation to get the maxterm equation.
 c. To draw the logic diagrams.
 d. To connect the circuits and evaluate them according
   to the truth tables.
 e. To compare the final results of the circuits.

MATERIALS:

 a. A 7404 hex inverter IC
 b. A 7408 quad two-input AND gate IC
 c. A 7432 quad two-input OR gate IC
 d. A 7400 quad two-input NAND gate IC
 e. A 7402 quad two-input NOR gate IC
 f. A 7486 Exclusive-OR gate IC

EQUIPMENT:

 a. Logic trainer

PROCEDURE:

Part I: The Exclusive-OR with Individual Gates

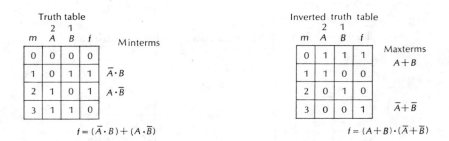

Truth table

m	A (2)	B (1)	f	Minterms
0	0	0	0	
1	0	1	1	$\bar{A}\cdot B$
2	1	0	1	$A\cdot\bar{B}$
3	1	1	0	

$$f = (\bar{A}\cdot B) + (A\cdot\bar{B})$$

Inverted truth table

m	A (2)	B (1)	f	Maxterms
0	1	1	1	$A + B$
1	1	0	0	
2	0	1	0	
3	0	0	1	$\bar{A}+\bar{B}$

$$f = (A+B)\cdot(\bar{A}+\bar{B})$$

Table 3-3 Truth Tables and Equations for the
Exclusive-OR

 a. Write the equation (see Table 3-3). From the table
   we get the minterm equation:
   (1) $f = (\bar{A}\cdot B)+(A\cdot\bar{B})$ (minterm)
   (2) $f = (A+B)\cdot(\bar{A}+\bar{B})$ (maxterm)
 b. Connect the minterm exclusive-OR gate circuit as
   shown in Figure 3-2. Complete the truth tables a and b.
 c. Connect the maxterm exclusive-OR circuit as shown in
   Figure 3-3. Complete truth tables a and b.

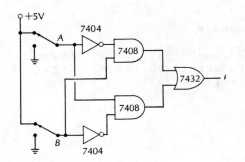

Truth table

m	A	B	f
0	0	0	0
1	0	1	1
2	1	0	1
3	1	1	0

a. AND-OR-NOT logic

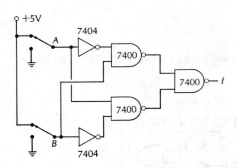

Truth table

m	A	B	f
0	0	0	0
1	0	1	1
2	1	0	1
3	1	1	0

b. NAND logic

Figure 3-2 Exclusive-OR Circuit (Minterm)
Equation: $f = \overline{A} \cdot B + A \cdot \overline{B}$

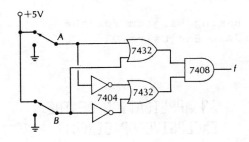

Truth table

m	A	B	f
0	0	0	0
1	0	1	1
2	1	0	1
3	1	1	0

a. AND-OR-NOT logic

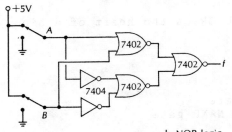

Truth table

m	A	B	f
0	0	0	0
1	0	1	1
2	1	0	1
3	1	1	0

b. NOR logic

Figure 3-3 Exclusive-OR Circuit (Maxterm)
Equation: $f = A + B \cdot \overline{A} + \overline{B}$

29

Part II: The Exclusive-OR Gate Package

    d. Connect the 7486 exclusive-OR package as shown in
       Figure 3-4 and complete the truth table. Figure 3-5
       is the basing diagram for the 7486

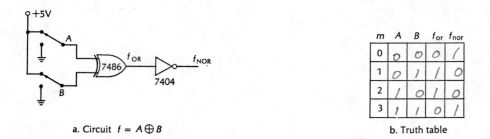

a. Circuit $f = A \oplus B$

m	A	B	f_{or}	f_{nor}
0	0	0	0	1
1	0	1	1	0
2	1	0	1	0
3	1	1	0	1

b. Truth table

Figure 3-4 The 7486 Exclusive-OR IC Package

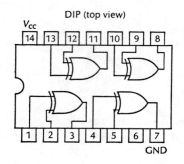

Figure 3-5 Basing Diagram for the
7486 Exclusive-OR

EXPERIMENT 3-2   AN APPLICATION OF THE EXCLUSIVE-OR CIRCUIT

OBJECTIVE:

    a. To study the exclusive-OR as the heart of a binary
       half adder.

MATERIALS:

    a. A 7404 hex inverter IC
    b. A 7486 exclusive-OR gate
    c. A 7400 quad two-input NAND gate

EQUIPMENT:

    a. Logic trainer

Part I: The Binary Half Adder

One of the primary functions any calculator or computer must perform is addition. Because digital circuits are two-state systems, arithmetic must be performed in a number system using base 2 or some coded base 2 system. We will examine more complex arithmetic elements and number systems in a later chapter.

The adder we will examine is called a half adder because it can add two binary digits (bits) but has no provision for a carry generated by a previous operation. As we will see later, two half adders can be combined to form a full adder that does have provision for the carry generated by a previous addition.

Table 3-4 shows the binary arithmetic table, the addition table written in truth table form, the exclusive (X-OR) truth table and the AND gate truth table. An examination of the tables (Table 3-4) reveals that the sum function is identical to the X-OR function and that an AND gate has the same truth table as the required carry function. In the experiment we will use a NAND gate and an inverter to perform the AND function.

m	$A+B$	sum	carry
0	0	0	0	0
1	0	1	1	0
2	1	0	1	0
3	1	1	0	1

a. Binary addition table

m	A	B	f_S	f_C
0	0	0	0	0
1	0	1	1	0
2	1	0	1	0
3	1	1	0	1

b. Binary addition table in truth table form

m	A	B	f
0	0	0	0
1	0	1	1
2	1	0	1
3	1	1	0

c. Exclusive-OR truth table (sum)

m	A	B	f
0	0	0	0
1	0	1	0
2	1	0	0
3	1	1	1

d. AND gate table (carry)

Table 3-4   Binary Addition Tables

PROCEDURE:

    a. Connect the circuit as shown in Figure 3-6.
    b. Complete the truth table in Figure 3-6.
    c. Compare the truth table in Figure 3-6 with
        those in Table 3-4.

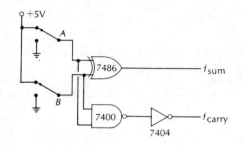

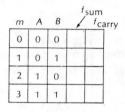

m	A	B	f_{sum}	f_{carry}
0	0	0		
1	0	1		
2	1	0		
3	1	1		

a. Circuit   b. Truth table

Figure 3-6   The Half Adder Circuit

PROBLEMS:

Given the truth table in Table 3-5:

a. Write the minterm equation.
b. Fill in table b and write the maxterm equation.
c. Draw the logic diagram for the equation in problem a.
d. Draw the logic diagram for the equation in problem b.

Part II: Simplification

Most circuits derived from the truth table contain far too much hardware. Here we will examine the method for reducing the hardware to a minimum for a given function. The following explains the underlying theory based on the Boolean law: $A + \overline{A} = 1$.

RULES FOR COMBINING TERMS

Two terms may be combined whenever:
a. each term contains exactly the same variables;
b. the terms to be combined are identical with the exception that one, and only one, variable appears in the complemented (barred) form in one term and in the uncomplemented form in the other.

Examples

1. $f = (A \cdot B \cdot C) + (\overline{A} \cdot B \cdot C)$. Because A appears in both the complemented and uncomplemented form and because $A + A = 1$, the A drops out leaving $f = (B \cdot C) + (B \cdot C)$. The two new terms are identical; one of them is said to be redundant and is dropped. The final simplified equation is $f = (B \cdot C)$.

2. Simplify the following equation by combining reducible pairs:
$f = (\overline{A} \cdot \overline{B} \cdot \overline{C}) + (\overline{A} \cdot B \cdot \overline{C}) + (\overline{A} \cdot \overline{B} \cdot C) + (\overline{A} \cdot B \cdot C)$
         1   2   3   4

32

a. If we combine terms 1 and 2:

$$\left. \begin{array}{c} \overline{A} \cdot \overline{B} \cdot \overline{C} \\ \overline{A} \cdot B \cdot \overline{C} \end{array} \right\} \overline{A} \cdot \overline{C}$$

b. If we combine terms 3 and 4:

$$\left. \begin{array}{c} \overline{A} \cdot \overline{B} \cdot C \\ \overline{A} \cdot B \cdot C \end{array} \right\} \overline{A} \cdot C$$

c. If we rewrite the equation using the simplified terms:

$$f = (\overline{A} \cdot \overline{C}) + (\overline{A} \cdot C)$$

d. On inspection we can see that these new terms can be combined to further simplify the equation:

$$\left. \begin{array}{c} \overline{A} \cdot \overline{C} \\ \overline{A} \cdot C \end{array} \right\} \overline{A}$$

e. The final equation reduces to $f = \overline{A}$, the equivalent of a single inverter for A.

Although the pairing process is a workable method, it is difficult to use and subject to errors when applied to more complex problems. A better method is the Karnaugh map. Table 3-6 shows two-, three-, and four-variable Karnaugh maps with the meaning of each square indicated. Normally these squares are left blank until ready for use. An examination of Table 3-6 will indicate that all adjacent squares represent reducible pairs.

m	A	B	f
0	0	0	1
1	0	1	0
2	1	0	1
3	1	1	1

m	A	B	f
0	1	1	
1	1	0	
2	0	1	
3	0	0	

a.   b.

Table 3-5   For Problems in Chapter 3

	AB	$\overline{A}B$	AB	$A\overline{B}$
$\overline{C}\overline{D}$	$\overline{A}\overline{B}\overline{C}\overline{D}$	$\overline{A}B\overline{C}\overline{D}$	$AB\overline{C}\overline{D}$	$A\overline{B}\overline{C}\overline{D}$
$\overline{C}D$	$\overline{A}\overline{B}\overline{C}D$	$\overline{A}B\overline{C}D$	$AB\overline{C}D$	$A\overline{B}\overline{C}D$
CD	$\overline{A}\overline{B}CD$	$\overline{A}BCD$	$ABCD$	$A\overline{B}CD$
$C\overline{D}$	$\overline{A}\overline{B}C\overline{D}$	$\overline{A}BC\overline{D}$	$ABC\overline{D}$	$A\overline{B}C\overline{D}$

	$\overline{A}$	A
$\overline{B}$	$\overline{A} \cdot \overline{B}$	$A \cdot \overline{B}$
B	$\overline{A} \cdot B$	$A \cdot B$

a. Two-variable Karnaugh map

	$\overline{A}\overline{B}$	$\overline{A}B$	AB	$A\overline{B}$
$\overline{C}$	$\overline{A}\overline{B}\overline{C}$	$\overline{A}B\overline{C}$	$AB\overline{C}$	$A\overline{B}\overline{C}$
C	$\overline{A}\overline{B}C$	$\overline{A}BC$	ABC	$A\overline{B}C$

b. Three-variable Karnaugh map

c. Four-variable Karnaugh maps

Table 3-6   Karnaugh Maps

USING THE KARNAUGH MAP

Looping Rules

1. Each loop should be drawn around the largest group of 2, 4, 8, and so on, adjacent entries possible. The number of entries in a loop must be a power of 2.
2. An entry may be involved in any number of loops, but a new loop should not be added unless it includes at least one entry not included in any other loops. Typical looping patterns are shown in Table 3-7.
3. After looping, inspect the map for any loop that encloses entries where all of the 1's in the loop are involved in other loops. Remove any such loops.

READING OUT THE SIMPLIFIED EQUATION

1. Each loop represents a new simplified minterm for the simplified equation. All simplified minterms will be OR'ed together.
2. Any variable in a given loop that appears in both the complemented and the uncomplemented form drops out.
3. The variables left in a loop make up the simplified term for that loop. Individual variables are AND'ed together.

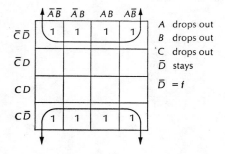

a. Example 1: edges adjacent

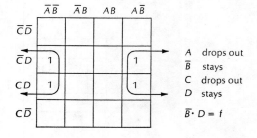

b. Example 2: edges adjacent

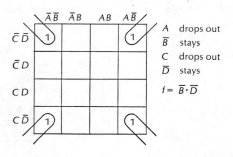

c. Example 3: corners adjacent (not diagonally)

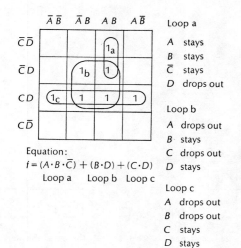

d. Example 4: overlapping bars

Table 3-7 Typical Looping Patterns

EXPERIMENT 3-3   COMPARING THE UNSIMPLIFIED AND SIMPLIFIED VERSIONS OF A CIRCUIT

OBJECTIVES:

a. To write the equation from the truth table.
b. To draw the logic diagrams.
c. To simplify the circuit in b using the Karnaugh map.
d. To connect the simplified circuit on the logic train-
    er and complete the functional truth table.
e. To compare the truth tables to determine if the two
    circuits are <u>functionally</u> the same.

MATERIALS:

a. A 7408 quad two-input AND gate
b. A 7432 quad two-input OR gate
c. A 7404 hex inverter

EQUIPMENT:

a. Logic trainer

	4 A	2 B	1 C	f	f_0	f_1
m_0	0	0	0	1		
m_1	0	0	1	1		
m_2	0	1	0	0		
m_3	0	1	1	1	$\leftarrow$	
m_4	1	0	0	0		
m_5	1	0	1	1		
m_6	1	1	0	0		
m_7	1	1	1	0		

Unsimplified equation:

$$\overline{A}\,\overline{B}\,\overline{C} + \overline{A}\,\overline{B}C + \overline{A}BC + A\overline{B}C$$

Table 3-8   Truth Table

PROCEDURE:

a. Given the truth table 3-8, write the minterm
    equation.

    Equation: $\overline{A}\,\overline{B}\,\overline{C} + \overline{A}\,\overline{B}C + \overline{A}BC + A\overline{B}C$

b. Draw the NAND logic diagram for the equation
    in a in the space provided in Figure 3-7.
c. Using the Karnaugh map in Table 3-9, simplify
    the equation in a.

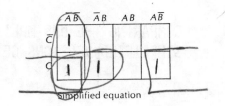

$\overline{A}\,\overline{B} + \overline{A}C + \overline{B}C$

Table 3-9   Karnaugh Map for
              Experiment 3-3

d. Draw the <u>simplified</u> logic diagram using NAND
    logic in Figure 3-8.

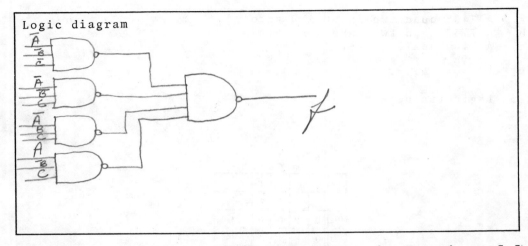

Figure 3-7   Unsimplified NAND Logic Diagram for Experiment 3-3

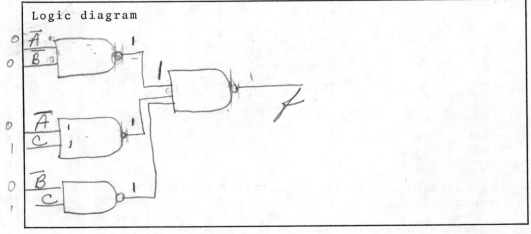

Figure 3-8   Simplified NAND Logic Diagram for Experiment 3-3

e. Construct the simplified NAND logic circuit on
    the trainer. Proceed through the combinations
    listed on the truth table (Table 3-8) and complete
    the f_0 column.

36

PROBLEMS:

a. Does the simplified circuit perform the same
function as the unsimplified version?

YES

b. What evidence is the above answer based upon?

upon actual, constructed circuit
↑simplified

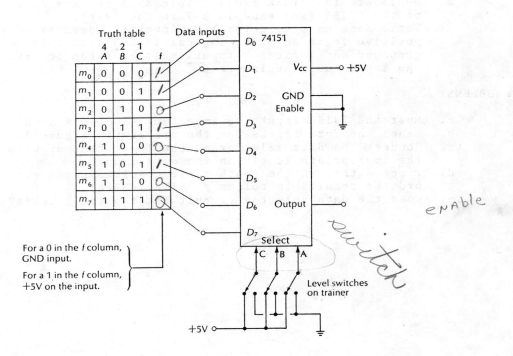

Truth table

	4 A	2 B	1 C	f
m_0	0	0	0	1
m_1	0	0	1	1
m_2	0	1	0	0
m_3	0	1	1	1
m_4	1	0	0	0
m_5	1	0	1	1
m_6	1	1	0	0
m_7	1	1	1	0

For a 0 in the f column,
GND input.

For a 1 in the f column,
+5V on the input.

enAble
switch

Figure 3-9 Data Selector/Multiplexer

Part III: Data Selector Logic

The data selector/multiplexer is a programmable logic package. In
this experiment we will use a data selector/multiplexer IC to implement the
function from the previous experiment. In this case simplification is not
necessary. Although more actual hardware will be involved as a result of
not simplifying, the hardware is already in the package. It costs nothing
extra, and because it is a one-package solution to the problem, it may be
cheaper than the simplified approach using individual gate packages. For
larger truth tables the data selector method is nearly always less expensive.

OBJECTIVES:

    a. To implement the circuit from the last experiment
       using a data selector/multiplexer.

    b. To compare the truth table for the data selector
       approach with the truth table for the discrete
       logic circuit in the previous experiment.

MATERIAL:

    a. A 74151 data selector/multiplexer

EQUIPMENT:

    a. Logic trainer

PROCEDURE:

    a. Duplicate the truth table (Table 3-8) as data inputs
       to the 74151 (see example 3-7 in the text).
       Note: Some data selectors are inverting devices. For
       positive logic outputs, logical 1 inputs must be
       grounded and logical 0 inputs must be taken to +5V.
       The inputs must be inverted.

PROBLEMS:

    a. Must the 74150 inputs be inverted? (See data book.)

    b. Label the data inputs for the problem in Figure 3-9.

    c. Connect the data selector on the logic trainer with
       the appropriate levels on the data inputs.

    d. Proceed through the truth table conditions and rec-
       ord the results in column f_1 (Table 3-8).

    e. Does the data selector circuit fit the truth table?

CHAPTER FOUR

FLIP-FLOPS AND LATCHES

Flip-flops and latches seem to be everywhere in digital circuits. They are found in counters, memories, registers that can move data from one place to another, arithmetic circuits, timing and pulse control circuits, frequency dividers, and many other places. Here we will experiment with the flip-flop elements that make up the basis of many of the systems to be examined later.

EXPERIMENT 4-1   THE SIMPLE NAND LATCH

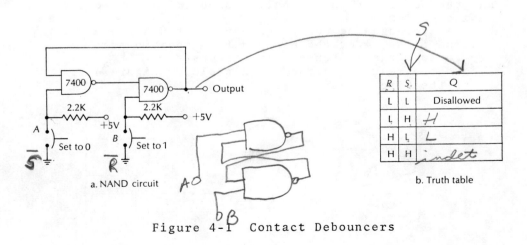

a. NAND circuit

b. Truth table

R	S.	Q
L	L	Disallowed
L	H	H
H	L	L
H	H	indet

Figure 4-1 Contact Debouncers

OBJECTIVE:

    a.   To examine behavior of the simple NAND latch used
        as a contact debouncing circuit.

MATERIAL:

    a.   A 7400 quad two-input NAND

EQUIPMENT:

    a.   Logic trainer

PROCEDURE:

    a.   Wire the circuit as shown in Figure 4-1. Follow
        the conditions through on Figure 4-1 and record the
        results on the truth table. Turn off the power
        supply momentarily and repeat the procedure.

EXPERIMENT 4-2   THE BASIC NAND R-S LATCH

OBJECTIVES:

    a.   To examine the behavior of the basic R-S NAND latch.
    b.   To plot that behavior on a truth table.

MATERIAL:

    a.   A 7400 quad two-input NAND

EQUIPMENT:

    a.   Logic trainer

PROCEDURE:

    a.   Connect the circuit as shown in Figure 4-2.
    b.   Connect the reset input to one logic level switch
        and the set input to another. Connect Q and $\bar{Q}$ to
        indicator lamps.
    c.   Proceed through the conditions on the truth table
        several times. For the H-H and L-L conditions,
        try to move the switches simultaneously.
    d.   Record the results on the truth table on Figure 4-2.
        Leave the circuit connected.

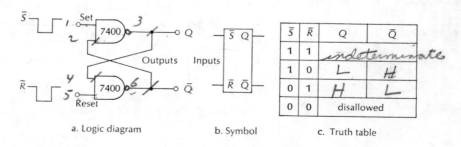

$\bar{S}$	$\bar{R}$	Q	$\bar{Q}$
1	1	*indeterminate*	
1	0	L	H
0	1	H	L
0	0	disallowed	

a. Logic diagram   b. Symbol   c. Truth table

Figure 4-2   NAND R-S Flip-Flop

40

EXPERIMENT 4-3   THE "D" LATCH

OBJECTIVES:

    a.   To observe the behavior of the "D" latch.
    b.   To plot the "D" latch behavior on a truth table.

PROCEDURE:

    a.   Connect the circuit as shown in Figure 4-3.
    b.   Complete the truth table. Connect the input to a level switch and $\underline{Q}$ $\overline{Q}$ to indicator lamps.

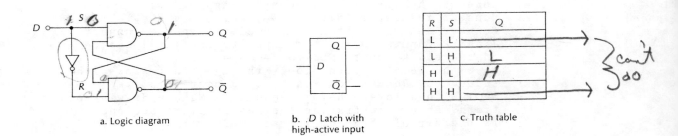

| a. Logic diagram | b. D Latch with high-active input | c. Truth table |

R	S	Q
L	L	
L	H	L
H	L	H
H	H	

Figure 4-3   NAND "D" Latch

PROBLEM:

    a.   How is the "D" latch behavior significantly different from that of the basic NAND R-S latch in experimental conditions? What conditions become impossible to obtain?

EXPERIMENT 4-4   THE J-K FLIP-FLOP, MASTER-SLAVE CONFIGURATION
(COMPOSED OF GATES)

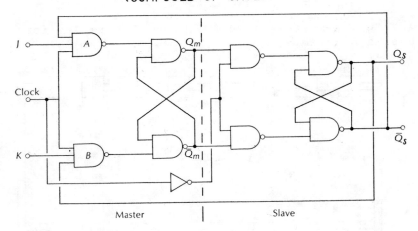

Figure 4-4   Master-Slave J-K Flip-Flop Logic Diagram

41

OBJECTIVE:

    a. To study the operating sequence of the master-slave
        flip-flop.

MATERIALS:

    a. A 7410 triple three-input NAND gate
    b. Two 7400 quad two-input NAND gates
    c. A 7404 hex inverter

EQUIPMENT:

    a. Logic trainer

PROCEDURE:

    a. Connect the circuit as shown in Figure 4-4.
    b. Connect indicator lamps to Q_m, $\overline{Q}_m$, Q_s, and $\overline{Q}_s$.
        Connect a level switch to the Clock input. Connect
        J and K inputs to +5V. Manipulate the level switch
        on the clock input until $Q_m = Q_s = 0$.
    c. Move the level switch slowly through a high-low-high
        sequence. Record the results. Repeat (from $Q_m = Q_s$
        = 0) with a low-high-low sequence. Make a drawing or
        truth table illustrating the master-slave sequence.
        Is the circuit high or low active?

        Note: If possible, leave the circuit connected and
        test the same conditions described in experiment 4-5.

EXPERIMENT 4-5   THE J-K FLIP-FLOP

OBJECTIVE:

    a. To evaluate the various operational modes of the
        J-K F-F.

MATERIAL:

    a. A 7476 J-K master-slave F-F. See Figure 4-5 for
        basing diagram.

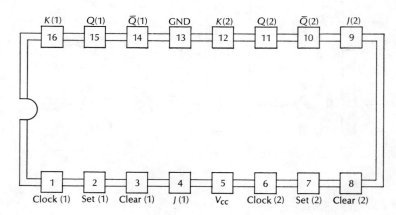

Figure 4-5   Basing Diagram for the 7476 Dual J-K Flip-Flop

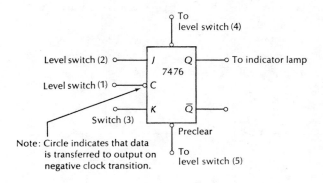

Level switch (2) J   Q   To indicator lamp
7476
Level switch (1) C
K   Q̄
Switch (3)

To level switch (4)

Preclear

To level switch (5)

Note: Circle indicates that data is transferred to output on negative clock transition.

Figure 4-6   J-K Flip-Flop

EQUIPMENT:

a. Logic trainer

PROCEDURE:

a. Connect the J-K master-slave F-F to logic level switches and indicator lamp as shown in Figure 4-6.
b. Connect the <u>preset</u> and <u>clear</u> lines to logic level switches. Set the preset to high. Move the clear switch to <u>low</u>, then back to <u>high</u>. Q should be resting at <u>low</u>.

Toggle Mode

c. Set J and K to <u>high</u> and set clock to <u>low</u> (Reset to Q = <u>low</u>, if necessary).

d. Move the clock switch from <u>low</u> to <u>high</u>.

What happened?

nothing

e. Move the clock switch to <u>low</u>.

What happened?

Q went from a low to a high

f. Repeat the clock level-switch sequence several times; this is the toggle mode.

g. Describe in detail the toggle mode behavior.

Clocked R-S Mode

h. Set the clock to <u>high</u>. Preset the F-F to Q = <u>high</u>.
i. Set J to <u>high</u> and $\overline{K}$ to <u>low</u>.

Describe the action:

Q stays high

j. Move the clock to <u>high</u> then back to <u>low</u>.

Describe the action:

Q stays high

k. Set K to <u>high</u> and J to <u>low</u>.

l. Move the clock to <u>high</u> then back to <u>low</u>.

Describe the action:

Q changed to low

m. Repeat steps i and j. Repeat the set-reset-clock sequence several times.

PROBLEMS:

a. Make a truth table for the J-K flip-flop.
b. Explain why all four possibilities on the J-K truth table are valid while some states in the R-S flip-flop are not,
c. How does the type "D" input configuration eliminate unwanted states?
d. If there are ten input pulses to a type "T" flip-flop, how many output pulses will result?

EXPERIMENT 4-6   EDGE-TRIGGERED TYPE "D"
CONNECTED AS A TYPE "T" FLIP-FLOP

OBJECTIVE:

    a. To observe the toggle action and frequency division action of an edge-triggered "D" flip-flop connected in a type "T" configuration.

MATERIAL:

    a. A 7474 dual "D" edge-triggered flip-flop

EQUIPMENT:

    a. Logic trainer
    b. CRO (dual trace)

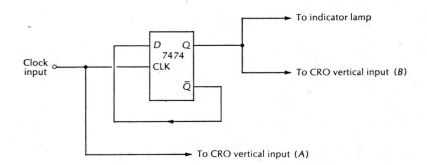

Figure 4-7   "D" Flip-Flop Connected as a Type "T"

PROCEDURE:

    a. Connect the circuit shown in Figure 4-7.
    b. Set the clock rate to approximately one pulse per second and observe the indicator lamp to ensure that the circuit is working.
    c. Increase the clock frequency to 1 kHz and plot the input and output waveforms on graph paper.

PROBLEM:

What is the input-output frequency relationship for the circuit in Figure 4-7?

the output frequency is one half the input frequency

45

CHAPTER FIVE

CLOCKS, PULSES AND
SIGNAL CONDITIONING

EXPERIMENT 5-1   PULSE MEASUREMENTS

OBJECTIVE:

    a. To become familiar with pulse parameters

MATERIALS:

    a. Ringing Coil - Broadcast Ferrite Ant. Coil

    b. Capacitor 220 pF

EQUIPMENT:

    a. Pulse generator $50 - 500\,\Omega\,Z_{out} \approx 5\mu$ sec pulse, with rise time less than 0.5μ sec. $E_{out} = 5$ to 10V.
    b. Resistance substitution box
    c. CRO with triggered sweep

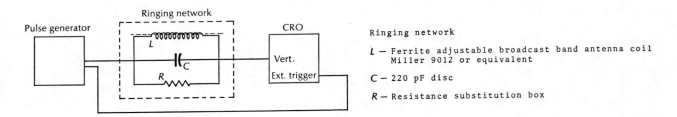

Figure 5-1 Circuits for Experiment 5-1

PROCEDURE:

    a. Connect the circuit as shown in Figure 5-1.

    b. Adjust the coil in the ringing network until the ringing (see Figure 5-2) is readable on the scope. Adjust the substitution box until the ringing is completely damped by the edge of the pulse. Note a lower resistance value reduces ringing amplitude and allows it to damp out earlier.

    c. Measure the parameters shown in Figure 5-2 and record all values on the drawing in that figure.

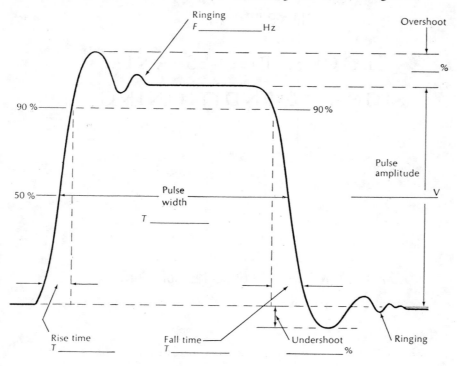

Figure 5-2 Non-Ideal Pulse for Experiment 5-1

Notes: _____

_____

_____

_____

_____

_____

_____

_____

_____

_____

_____

THE SCHMITT TRIGGER

The Schmitt trigger is a regenerative, level-sensitive switching circuit. It has a turn-on threshold and a lower value turn-off threshhold. The difference between the two threshold voltages is called the hysteresis voltage.

The circuit is used to shape slow-rising signals (such as sine and sawtooth voltages) into digitally compatible pulses. The regenerative action forces a fast rise, simulating a typical digital pulse rise time. The hysteresis provides a guard band that greatly reduces the susceptibility to noise and signal amplitude variations.

EXPERIMENT 5-2   THE SCHMITT TRIGGER

OBJECTIVES:

    a. To measure the Schmitt hysteresis "band".
    b. To observe and plot the waveform for input and output when the input waveform is sinusoidal.

MATERIALS:

    a. A 7413 quad Schmitt NAND gate IC, or 7414 hex Schmitt inverter
    b. A 1000 ohm 5-10 turn linear potentiometer
    c. A 560 ohm resistor
    d. Two 1KΩ resistors
    e. Two silicon small signal diodes 1N914 or equivalent.

EQUIPMENT:

    a. Logic trainer
    b. CRO, triggered-sweep dual-trace
    c. 6-10V AC signal source (a 6.3V filament transformer connected to a Variac is adequate)

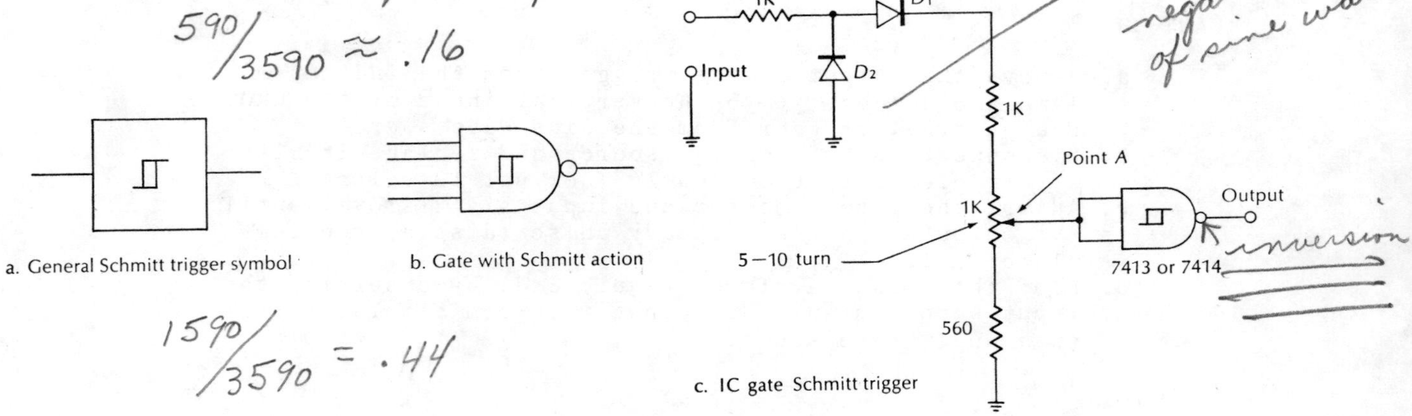

Vin when input is positive

$$\frac{590}{3590} \approx .16$$

chips off negative part of sine wave

a. General Schmitt trigger symbol   b. Gate with Schmitt action   c. IC gate Schmitt trigger

$$\frac{1590}{3590} = .44$$

inversion

Figure 5-3   Schmitt Trigger Symbols and IC Gate Schmitt Trigger

PROCEDURE:

Part I

a. Connect the circuit as shown in Figure 5-3c.
b. Connect a 5-10V DC supply to input and GND + to input. Connect the output of the Schmitt trigger to an indicator lamp on the logic trainer.
c. Adjust the potentiometer until the lamp just fires. Measure the voltage at point A (referenced to GND). Record the voltage on Table 5-1, UTL (upper trip level).
d. Adjust the potentiometer back until the lamp just goes out. Record this voltage on Table 5-1, LTL (lower trip level).
e. Compute the hysteresis voltage:

$$V_{hysteresis} = UTL-LTL.$$

Record the result.

	UTL	LTL
Voltage at point A	1.9 V	1.24 V
Computed hysteresis voltage	.66 V	

Typically

$\approx .8V$

Table 5-1 For Experiment 5-2, Part I

PART II

a. Remove the output of the trigger from the indicator lamp and connect it to the vertical input of the CRO. Use external trigger from the sine wave source.
b. Disconnect the DC voltage source and replace it with a variable voltage AC source (nominal 10 volts).
c. Adjust the potentiometer and input signal level until the output is a clean steady pulse (display two complete cycles).
d. Plot the pulse waveform (Figure 5-4) by observing the input waveform and the output waveform simultaneously on a dual trace scope.

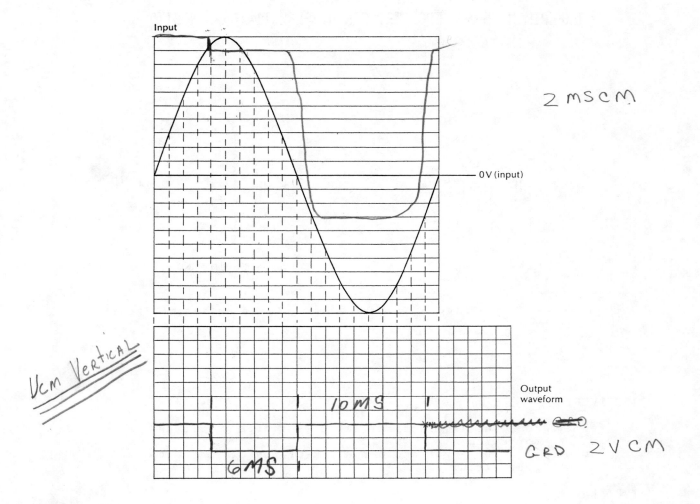

Figure 5-4 For Experiment 5-2, Part II

PROBLEMS:

   a. What is the output pulse amplitude? (in volts)?

_____

   b. Is the pulse positive? Negative? Both?

_____

   c. What is the pulse width?

   P_W _____

51

EXPERIMENT 5-3   EDGE-TRIGGER DIFFERENTIATOR CIRCUITS

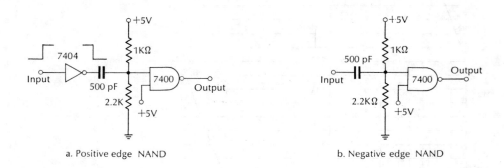

Figure 5-5 Edge-Triggering Pulses Using Differentiator Circuit

OBJECTIVES:

a.   To construct a practical TTL edge-trigger differen-
     tiator circuit.
b.   To plot the input and output waveforms of the edge-
     trigger circuit.

MATERIALS:

a.   A 7400 quad NAND gate
b.   A 7404 hex inverter
c.   A resistor 1 KΩ
d.   A resistor 2.2 KΩ
e.   A 500 pF disc capacitor

EQUIPMENT:

a.   Logic trainer
b.   Dual trace CRO

PROCEDURE:

a.   Connect the circuits as shown in Figure 5-5a and b.
b.   Connect a TTL compatible pulse of approximately 1
     kHz to the input of circuit a.
c.   Connect the CRO dual trace to the input and output.
d.   Plot the input and output waveforms on a sheet of
     graph paper.
e.   Repeat for circuit b.

PROBLEM:

a.   Explain why this is called an edge-triggered circuit.
     Base your answer on the waveforms you have plotted.

52

EXPERIMENT 5-4   THE TRANSISTOR ASTABLE MULTIVIBRATOR

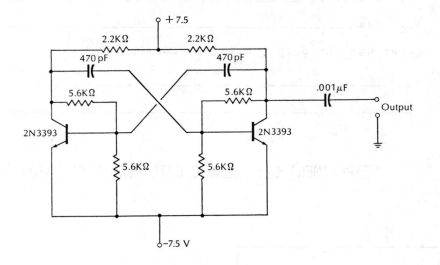

Figure 5-6   Astable Multivibrator

OBJECTIVES:

    a. To construct a transistor as table multivibrator.
    b. To observe and record the collector and base wave-
        forms.

MATERIALS:

    a. Two transistors 2N3393 or any similar NPN transistor
    b. Two resistors 2.2 KΩ
    c. Four resistors 5.6 KΩ
    d. Two capacitors 470 pF
    e. One capacitor .001 μF

EQUIPMENT:

    a. +7.5 volt and -7.5 volt power supply
    b. CRO

PROCEDURE:

    a. Connect the circuit as shown in Figure 5-6.
    b. Using a CRO, observe the output waveform and record it
        on a sheet of graph paper.
    c. Observe the waveforms at both bases and both collectors;
        sketch one of each on graph paper.
    d. Measure and record the output signal frequency.
    e. Change one of the 470 pF capacitors to 1000 pF and
        observe the output waveform.

PROBLEMS:

  a. Where was the zero reference line on each of the
      following waveforms?

    a. Output _____

    b. Collector _____

    c. Base _____

  b. What was the output waveform amplitude?

      _____

      _____

EXPERIMENT 5-5   LOGIC GATE RING OSCILLATOR

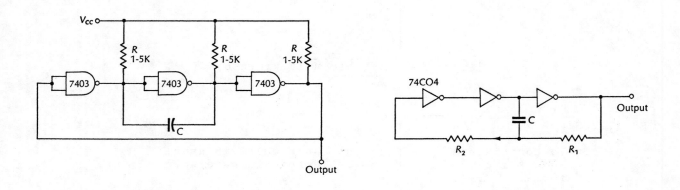

a. Practical ring oscillator using 7403 open collector NAND gate   b. C-MOS oscillator

Figure 5-7 Two Types of Ring Oscillators

OBJECTIVES:

  a. To construct a logic gate ring oscillator.
  b. To observe and record the output waveform.
  c. To construct a table of frequency vs. capacitance
      values.

MATERIALS:

  TTL Version

  a. A 7403 open collector quad NAND
  b. Three 1.5 KΩ resistors
  c. Capacitor values: .0033, .033, .33, 3, 25, 250 μF

C-MOS Version

    a. A 74C04 C-MOS hex inverter
    b. Two resistors 22 KΩ
    c. Capacitors from TTL list

EQUIPMENT:

    a. Logic trainer
    b. CRO

PROCEDURE:

    a. Construct the circuit in Figure 5-7a or b.
    b. Measure the output frequency and sketch the waveform for each capacitor value shown in Table 5-2.

Measured frequency	Capacitor size, μF	Waveform shape
	250. μFD	
	25. - μFD	
	3.0 - μFD	
	.33 - μFD	
	.033 - μFD	
	.0033- μFD	

Table 5-2 Frequency Table for the Ring Oscillator

PROBLEMS:

    a. How does the (approximately) 1 kHz waveform of the logic gate oscillator compare with the output waveform of the transistor astable?
    b. At what frequencies is the waveform most nearly square?
    c. Find the equation in the text that gives the frequency for the ring oscillator and compare calculated values with your experimental results.

EXPERIMENT 5-6   THE 74121 MONOSTABLE (ONE-SHOT)

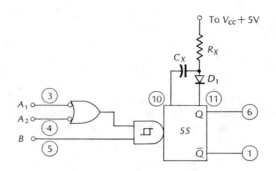

Note: To use the 2K internal timing resistor, omit
R_x and connect pin (9) to pin (14)

V_{cc} = pin (14)

GND = pin (7)

D_1 = silicon switching diode

Figure 5-8   The 74121 Monostable

The 74121 is a complete one-shot circuit with the exception of an external timing resistor and capacitor. The circuit features a built-in Schmitt trigger. The two inputs A_1 and A_2 require rise rates in excess of 1 volt/microsecond. These are low activated OR inputs and either or both can initiate the one-shot if input B is high.

Input B is the Schmitt triggered input and can respond to rise rates as low as 1 volt per second. The B input is responsive as long as A_1 or A_2 (or both) is at logic 0 (GND).

The IC can produce output pulse widths of from 40 ns to 40 seconds, depending on timing component values.

OBJECTIVES:

    a.   To examine the 74121 as a pulse stretcher.
    b.   To study the nonretriggerable action of the 74121.
    c.   To use the 74121 to delay and shorten a pulse.
    d.   To examine the astable multivibrator using 74121 one-shots.

MATERIALS:

    a.   Two 74121 monostable IC's
    b.   Two of any silicon switching diodes
    c.   A capacitor 10 μF
    d.   Two resistors 40 KΩ
    e.   Two capacitors .022 μF
    f.   Miscellaneous student selected resistors and capacitors

EQUIPMENT:

    a. Logic trainer
    b. CRO, triggered sweep, dual trace

  Note: Leave the 74121 circuit connected for part II.

PROCEDURE:

Part I Pulse Stretcher

    a. Connect the circuit as shown in Figure 5-8.
    b. Give the approximation:

$P_w = 0.7 \, R_x C_x$ (R in ohms, C in farads, pulse width in seconds)

Calculate: P_w when $C_x = 10\mu F$ and $R_x = 40 \, K\Omega$

$P_w =$ _____

    c. Connect the output (pin 6) to an indicator lamp on the trainer.
    d. Connect input B to +5V.
    e. Connect the normally high (NH) of the bounceless pushbutton (from Figure 4-1) to A_1 and A_2 inputs of Figure 5-8.
    f. Momentarily depress and then release the pushbutton rapidly and observe the indicator lamp.
    g. Does the on time of the indicator agree with the calculated value for P_w ?

Calculated P_w _____

Timed lamp on time: _____

Explain what is taking place: _____

_____

_____

_____

_____

_____

PROBLEM:

    a. Suggest an application for a circuit with such a long delay period:

_____

_____

_____

_____

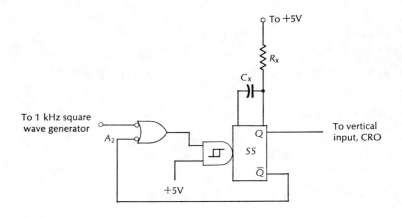

Figure 5-9   Nonretriggerable Operation
of the 74121 One-Shot

PROCEDURE:

Part II   Nonretriggerable Operation of the 74121

    a.   Reconfigure the circuit as shown in Figure 5-9.
    b.   Calculate values for R_x and C_x to yield a delay equal
        to 4-6 complete cycles for a 1 kHz square wave pulse.
        Use: $P_w \approx 0.7\ RC$.
    c.   Install the calculated values for C_x and R_x (see
        Figure 5-9).
    d.   Connect the output to one vertical input channel of
        the CRO.
    e.   Connect a 1 kHz square wave (0 to +5V amplitude) to
        the input. The clock on the trainer can be used.
    f.   Connect a (+) external trigger from the square wave
        generator (clock) to the scope external trigger.
    g.   Plot the waveforms (input and output) on graph paper.

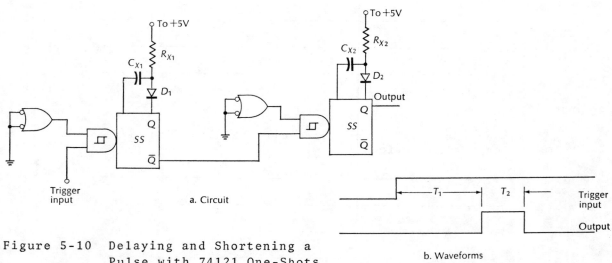

a. Circuit

b. Waveforms

Figure 5-10   Delaying and Shortening a
Pulse with 74121 One-Shots

58

Part III Delaying and Shortening a Pulse Using the 74121 One-Shot

    a. Construct the circuit shown in Figure 5-10.
    b. Using a 1 kHz or a 10 kHz square wave for trigger input, compute delays T_1 and T_2 to yield proportions similar to those shown in Figure 5-10b. Enter the delay times in the spaces provided on Figure 5-10b.
    c. Connect the output of the circuit in Figure 5-10 to one vertical input channel on the CRO.
    d. Connect the output square wave generator to the input of the circuit and to the second vertical input channel of the CRO.
    e. Plot the input and output timing diagram on graph paper.

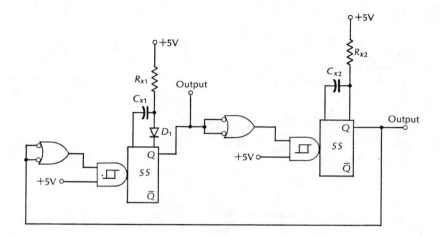

Figure 5-11 Astable Multivibrator from 74121 One-Shots

Part IV The One-Shot Multivibrator Using 74121's

    a. Construct the circuit in Figure 5-11.
    b. Select values of C_x and R_x for any desired frequency: $f = \frac{1}{T}$, $T = 1.4\ RC$, for $C_{x1} = C_{x2}$ and $R_{x1} = R_{x2}$.
    c. Observe the output waveform from both outputs and plot them on graph paper.

EXPERIMENT 5-7   THE 555 ASTABLE CIRCUIT

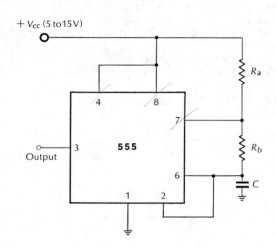

a. The circuit

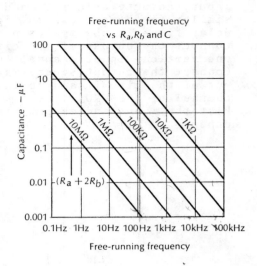

b. Free running frequency nomogram for the 555 astable circuit

Figure 5-12   The 555 Timer Connected in an Astable Configuration

OBJECTIVES:

    a.   To configure the 555 timer in its astable mode.
    b.   To examine and record waveforms.
    c.   To check the frequency nomogram in a practical situation.

MATERIALS:

    a.   A 555 timer
    b.   Miscellaneous resistors and capacitors (student selected)

EQUIPMENT:

    a.   Logic trainer
    b.   CRO

PROCEDURE:

    a.   Using the nomogram (Figure 5-12b), complete the component value listings in Table 5-3.
    b.   Connect the circuit in Figure 5-12 using each set of values in Table 5-3.
    c.   Measure the frequency for each set of values and record them on the table.

Component values			Calculated frequency	Measured frequency	% of error between measured & Calculated
R_a	R_b	C			
2.2k	1M	.01	95 HZ	79 HZ	17%
2.2K	1M	.001	900 HZ	778 HZ	14%
2.2K	100K	.001	8000 HZ	8148 HZ	¢2%
10K	100	.001	7500 HZ	788 8HZ	5%
10K	10K	.01	7000 HZ	5530 HZ	21%
10K	10K	.001	55300 HZ	49473 HZ	11%

Table 5-3 555 Frequency Table

PROBLEM:

    a. Compute the percentage of error for each frequency
       in Table 5-3.

CHAPTER SIX

ENCODERS, DECODERS, AND PARITY DETECTORS

EXPERIMENT 6-1 THE PARITY DETECTOR

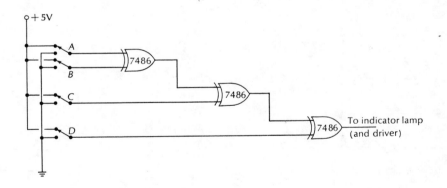

Figure 6-1 Circuit for Parity Detector
(for Experiment 6-1)

When using error detecting codes with even or odd parity, it is necessary to have a circuit to determine whether the parity is correct for each group of bits. If parity is incorrect, it indicates that a bit has been dropped or added as a machine error. The following experiment involves a simple parity detector using exclusive-OR gates.

OBJECTIVE:

  a. To examine the exclusive-OR parity detector circuit.

MATERIAL:

  a. A 7486 quad two-input exclusive-OR IC

EQUIPMENT:

  a. Logic trainer

PROCEDURE:

  a. Connect the circuit as shown in Figure 6-1 and complete the table (Table 6-1).

Table 6-1

Parity Table for
Experiment 6-1

Code Group	Parity Odd–Even	Number of ones in Code Group
A B C D	Parity	No. of 1's
1 0 0 0		
0 1 1 0		
1 1 0 1		
0 0 0 1		
0 0 1 1		
1 0 0 1		

EXPERIMENT 6-2   THE DIODE ENCODING MATRIX

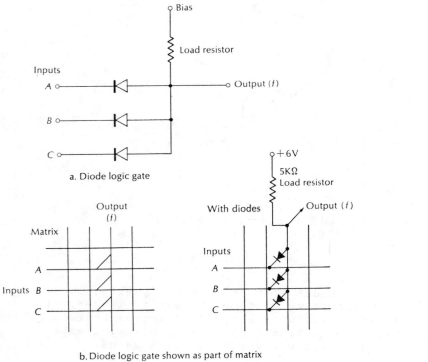

a. Diode logic gate

b. Diode logic gate shown as part of matrix

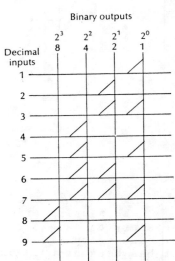

c. Decimal to binary encoder matrix

Figure 6-2   Decimal-to-Binary Encoder Matrix

64

The diode matrix uses diode logic gates (a forerunner of TTL) to form an encoding matrix. The technique is used less frequently than it once was, but it still finds application in peripheral devices such as printers, where power levels are much too high for TTL. The circuit we will examine here encodes decimal into binary. Diode decoders are sometimes found as well.

OBJECTIVE:

    a. To verify the operation of the diode encoder matrix.

MATERIALS:

    a. Fifteen silicon diodes (1N914)
    b. Four 2.2 KΩ resistors

EQUIPMENT:

    a. Logic trainer
    b. Variable voltage DC power supply

PROCEDURE:

    a. Connect the matrix with diodes located as shown in Figure 6-2c.
    b. Connect nine level switches to the decimal inputs.
    c. Connect indicator lamps to each of the four outputs.
    d. Connect the "bias" end of all resistors in the matrix to +6 volts.

        Note: It may be necessary to make a slight adjustment in the bias power supply voltage for proper operation.

    e. Set all input level switches to low.
    f. Proceed from 1 through 9, moving the level switch to +5, recording the output conditions on Table 6-2, and returning the switch to ground. Complete Table 6-2.

Decimal input	Binary Outputs			
	8	4	2	1
0				
1				
2				
3				
4				
5				

Table 6-2   Table of Results for Experiment 6-2

PROBLEMS:

    a. Does the encoder provide true binary equivalents (outputs) of the decimal inputs?
    b. Is the voltage (bias) critical? Why?
    c. Draw the circuit equivalent of the encoder using standard logic gates.

EXPERIMENT 6-3 TWO-LINE TO FOUR-LINE DECODER

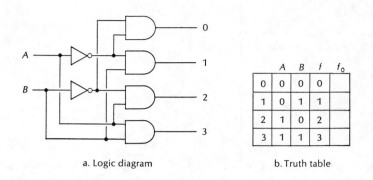

	A	B	f	f_0
0	0	0	0	
1	1	0	1	
2	1	0	2	
3	1	1	3	

a. Logic diagram   b. Truth table

Figure 6-3   Two-Line to Four-Line Decoder

OBJECTIVE:

    a. To construct and evaluate a two-line to four-line decoder.

MATERIALS:

    a. A 7408 quad two-input AND gate
    b. A 7404 hex inverter

EQUIPMENT:

    a. Logic trainer

PROCEDURE:

    a. Connect the circuit as shown in Figure 6-3.
    b. Connect inputs A and B to level switches.
    c. Connect the outputs to indicator lamps.
    d. Proceed through the conditions shown on the truth table (Figure 6-3b) and record the output conditions in the f_0 column.

PROBLEM:

    a. Draw the circuit in Figure 6-3 using NAND gates.

CHAPTER SEVEN

COUNTERS

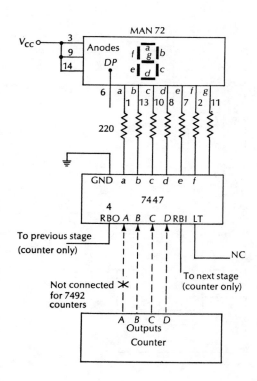

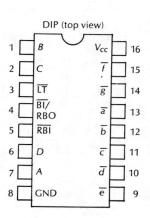

Figure 7-1   Decoder Display Circuit

In this chapter we will frequently use simultaneous readout methods: individual lamps (with lamp drivers) on each counter output (where applicable) and a decoded BCD seven-segment readout. In frequency divider experiments the CRO will become the most common readout device.

Before you begin the experiments, hook up the circuit in Figure 7-1.

1. Connect the lamp test input to switch connected to provide either +5 or GND potential.
2. Connect inputs A, B, C, D to floating terminals to accept input data from the counters that you will be experimenting with.
3. Connect a lead from each input of the 7447 decoder in Figure 7-1 to an indicator lamp on the trainer. These indicator lamps will provide 0 or 1 indications for each counter output. The LED will display a decoded seven-segment readout as the decimal equivalent of the binary states of the counter.
4. Leave the circuit of Figure 7-1 connected for the balance of the experiments in this chapter and the next.

EXPERIMENT 7-1   THE BINARY RIPPLE UP COUNTER

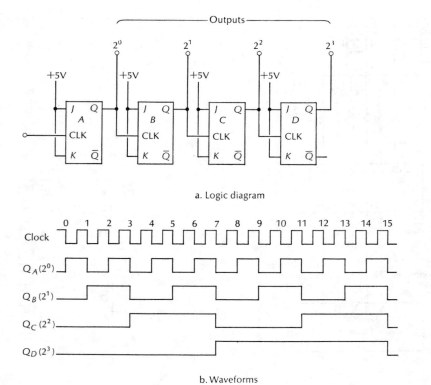

a. Logic diagram

b. Waveforms

Figure 7-2   Binary Ripple Counter (Up Counter, Asynchronous)

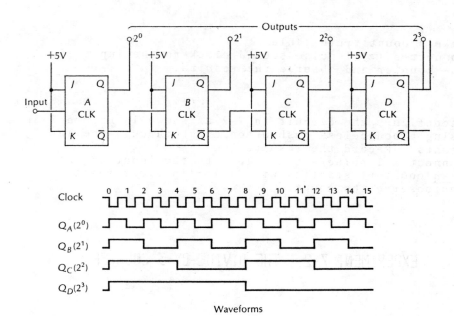

Figure 7-3   Binary Ripple Down Counter

The binary ripple counter is the most basic and simplest of binary counters. Its counting rate is also the lowest of all counters and is reduced as the length of the counting chain is increased. In spite of these limitations, it is a frequently encountered circuit. It is as useful a counter as the more complex, faster counters whenever high counting speeds are not required.

OBJECTIVE:

    a. To observe the <u>action</u> of the binary ripple counter.

MATERIALS:

    a. Two 7476 dual master-slave J-K flip-flops
    b. Miscellaneous interconnecting leads

EQUIPMENT:

    a. Logic trainer

PROCEDURE:

Part I
    a. Connect the circuit as shown in Figure 7-2.
    b. Connect outputs A, B, C, and D to the corresponding A, B, C, and D inputs of the 7447 decoder.
    c. Connect the clock input line to a bounceless pushbutton.
    d. Advance the count slowly by successive pushbutton actuations. Record the state of the indicator lamps (lit = 1, dark = 0) at each output (A, B, C, D) of the counter.
    e. Record the LED display (illuminated segments) conditions.

      f.   Make a count truth table.

      g.   Connect a (≈) 1 pulse/second clock to the input of
           the counter and observe the results.

Part II

      h.   Reconfigure the circuit in 7-2 as shown in Figure 7-3.

      i.   Using a bounceless pushbutton, clock through the 16
           counts. Record the results.

      j.   Connect a 1 pulse/second clock to the input of the
           <u>down</u> counter, starting with all flip-flops reset,
           and observe the count.

EXPERIMENT 7-2   THE DIVIDE-BY-3 COUNTER

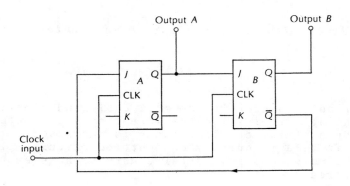

Figure 7-4   Mod 3 Counter

OBJECTIVES:

      a.   To observe the behavior of a divide-by-3 counter.

      b.   To plot the truth table for the divide-by-3 counter.

      c.   To determine what to do with unused decoder inputs.

MATERIALS:

      a.   A 7476 dual master-slave J-K flip-flop

      b.   Miscellaneous interconnecting leads

EQUIPMENT:

      a.   Logic trainer

PROCEDURE:

      a.   Connect the circuit as shown in Figure 7-4.

      b.   Connect QA and QB to the A and B inputs of the
           decoder (Figure 7-1).

      c.   Determine the logic condition for unused inputs
           on the decoder.

      d.   Construct a count truth table.

PROBLEMS:

    a. What proved to be the proper thing to do with unused decoder inputs?

    b. Would leaving unused decoder leads open be a good idea? Why or why not?

EXPERIMENT 7-3   THE DIVIDE-BY-5 COUNTER

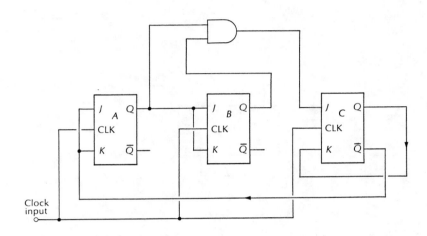

Figure 7-5 Synchronous Mod 5 Counter

OBJECTIVES:

    a. To observe the count behavior of a divide-by-5 counter.

    b. To plot the truth table for the divide-by-5 counter.

MATERIALS:

    a. Two 7476 dual master-slave J-K flip-flops.

    b. A 7400 quad NAND connected as an AND gate

EQUIPMENT:

    a. Logic trainer

    b. CRO dual trace triggered sweep

PROCEDURE:

    a. Connect the circuit as shown in Figure 7-5.

    b. Connect QA, QB, QC to the inputs A, B, C of the decoder-display circuit (Figure 7-1).

c. Observe the count sequence using the bounceless push-button. Make a count truth table.
d. Disconnect the divide-by-5 counter from the display and connect QC to one vertical input on a CRO.
e. Connect a 1kHz clock to the input of the counter and to the second vertical input on the CRO.
f. Derive external trigger from clock.
g. Plot the clock and counter waveforms.

EXPERIMENT 7-4   THE 7493 BINARY RIPPLE COUNTER

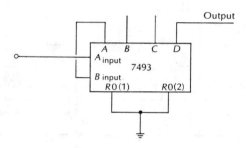

Figure 7-6   Divide-by-16 Ripple Counter
Using the 54/7493

OBJECTIVE:

a. To observe the operation of the 7493 counter in a divide-by-16 mode.

MATERIAL:

a. A 7493 binary <u>up</u> counter

EQUIPMENT:

a. Logic trainer
b. CRO, dual trace

PROCEDURE:

a. Connect the 7493 counter as shown in Figure 7-6.
b. Connect the A, B, C, D outputs of the 7493 to the decoder-display circuit.
c. Connect the bounceless pushbutton and step the counter through its cycle. Make a count truth table.
d. Disconnect the bounceless pushbutton and connect the input of the counter to a 1 second clock and observe the count sequence.

72

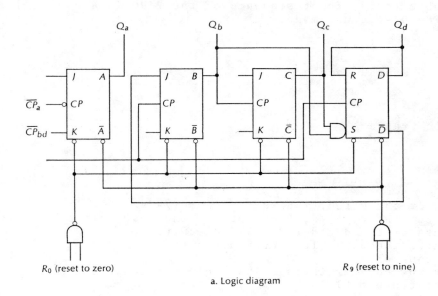

a. Logic diagram

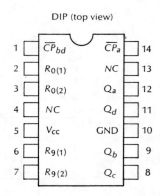

Logic symbol

5490, 7490

V_{cc} = Pin 5
GND = Pin 10
NC = Pins 4,13

DIP (top view)

1	$\overline{CP}_{bd}$	$\overline{CP}_a$	14
2	$R_{0(1)}$	NC	13
3	$R_{0(2)}$	Q_a	12
4	NC	Q_d	11
5	V_{cc}	GND	10
6	$R_{9(1)}$	Q_b	9
7	$R_{9(2)}$	Q_c	8

b. Basing diagram and symbol

Outputs

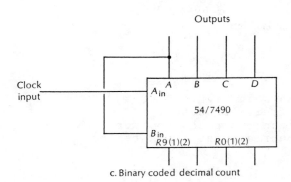

Clock
input

A_{in}

B_{in}

$R9(1)(2)$ $R0(1)(2)$

54/7490

c. Binary coded decimal count

Figure 7-7   Logic Diagram for the
54/7490 Decade Counter

73

OBJECTIVES:

    a.   To observe the two divide-by-10 count modes of the 7490 decade counter.

    b.   To observe the count sequence of the 7490 in a divide-by-6 count mode.

MATERIAL:

    a.   A 7490 decade counter

EQUIPMENT:

    a.   Logic trainer

PROCEDURE:

Part I The BCD Count Sequence

    a.   Connect the circuit shown in Figure 7-7c.

    b.   Connect the A, B, C, D outputs of the 7490 to the inputs of the decoder display circuit.

    c.   Connect the bounceless pushbutton to the input of the counter.

    d.   Walk the counter through its cycle and construct a count truth table.

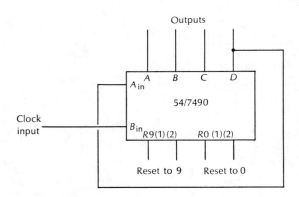

Figure 7-8 Symmetrical Divide-by-10 Mod
Using the 54/7490

Part II The Symmetrical Count Sequence

    e.   Reconfigure Figure 7-7 as shown in Figure 7-8. Leave the decoder display circuit connected.

    f.   Using the bounceless pushbutton, step the counter through its cycle and construct a count truth table.

74

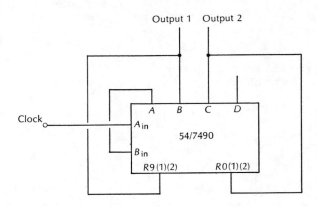

Figure 7-9 The 54/7490 Configured as
a Divide-by-6 Counter

Part III : The 7490 Connected as a Divide-by-6 Mode

g. Reconfigure the circuit as shown in Figure 7-9.
    Leave the decoder display circuit connected.
h. Step the counter through its count sequence and
    construct a count truth table.
i. Disconnect the bounceless pushbutton from the input
    of the counter and connect a 1 pulse per second clock
    to the counter input. Observe the results.

EXPERIMENT 7-6   THE 74161 PRESETTABLE COUNTER

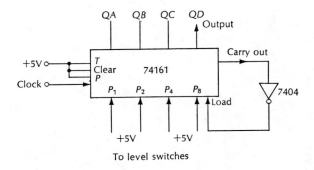

Figure 7-10   The 74161

OBJECTIVES:

    a.   To study the counting behavior of a presettable counter.
    b.   To observe the various counting sequences.

MATERIALS:

    a.   A 74161 presettable counter
    b.   A 7404 hex inverter

EQUIPMENT:

    a.   Logic trainer

PROCEDURE:

    a.   Connect the 74161 counter and 7404 inverter as shown.
    b.   Connect P_1, P_2, P_4, and P_8 to level switches.
    c.   Connect a slow clock or debounced pushbutton to the clock input.
    d.   Connect QA, QB, QC and QD to indicator lamps.
    e.   Set the logic level switches at random and observe the count. Select two conditions and make truth tables for them.

PROBLEMS:

    a.   Were there any conditions tried that counted out of the usual binary order?
    b.   Would this circuit be acceptable for use with seven-segment readouts? Why?
    c.   Suggest some applications for this kind of counter.

CHAPTER EIGHT

SHIFT REGISTERS AND
SHIFT REGISTER COUNTERS

EXPERIMENT 8-1   THE VARIOUS MODES OF·OPERATION
OF THE 7495 SHIFT REGISTER

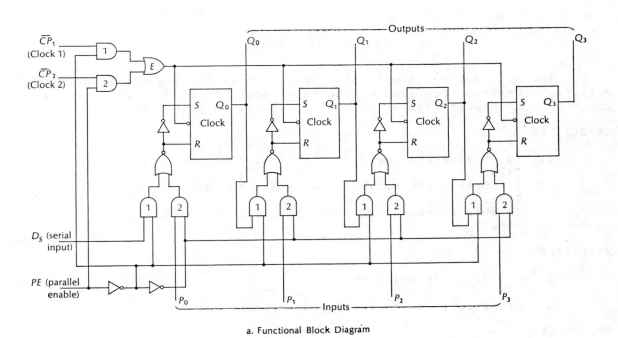

a. Functional Block Diagram

Figure 8-1   The 54/7495 Right/Left Shift Register

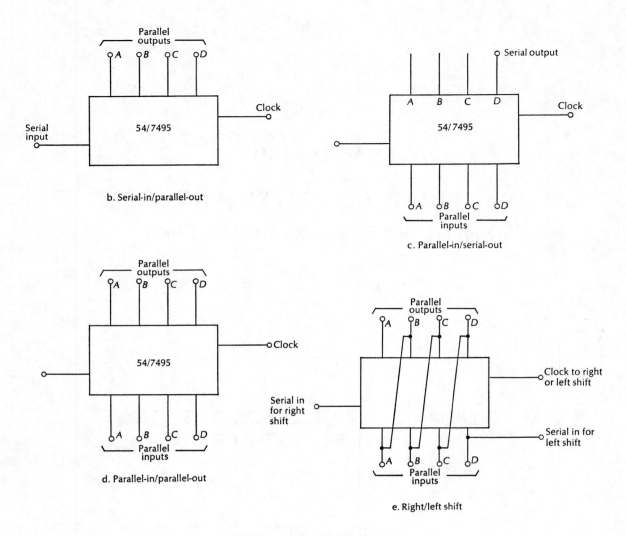

Figure 8-1 continued

In this chapter we will experiment with shift registers and shift register counters. For some of the experiments in this chapter we will use the same decoder-display circuit as that used in Chapter 7.

OBJECTIVES:

    a. To observe the serial-in/parallel-out mode of the 7495.

    b. To observe the parallel-in/serial-out mode of the 7495.

    c. To observe the parallel-in/parallel-out mode of the 7495.

MATERIALS:

    a. A 7495 shift register

    b. Extra level switches if needed (total of six required).

EQUIPMENT:

    a. Logic trainer

PROCEDURE:

a. The logic diagram and basing diagram for the 7495 are shown in Figure 8-1. Connect clocks 1 and 2 together and to the bounceless pushbutton.
b. Connect P_0, P_1, P_2, and P_3 to level switches.
c. Connect the serial input and the parallel-enable input to level switches.
d. Connect the outputs Q_0, Q_1, Q_2, and Q_3 to indicator lamps.

Part I: Serial and Parallel Loading

e. Set parallel-enable level (mode) switch to <u>low</u>.
f. Set serial input to <u>low</u>.
g. Set parallel input level switches to logical 0.
h. Turn on the power and clock 0's through until all outputs are at logical zero.
i. Move the serial input level switch to logical 1 and clock the 1 into the first flip-flop of the register.
j. Return the serial input level switch to logical 0.
k. Clock the 1 through the register and observe its progress.
l. Load two 1's using the serial input. Clock them through.

Parallel Loading

m. Set the mode switch (parallel enable) to logical 1.
n. Use the parallel entry level switches on P_0, P_1, P_2, and P_3 to load two 1's into the register.
o. Set the mode switch back to logical 0 and clock the data through the register.
p. Summarize the results.

Part II: Left/right Shifting with the 7495 Shift Register

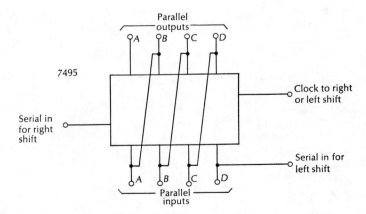

Figure 8-2 External Connections for Right/Left Shift

79

PROCEDURE:

    a.   Make external connections as shown in Figure 8-2.
    b.   The indicator lamp circuit remains connected.
    c.   The clock inputs can remain connected as they were in the previous example.
    d.   Connect the "serial in for left shift" line (on parallel input D) to a level switch. The parallel entry level switches for A, B, and C parallel entry inputs are disconnected for this experiment.
    e.   Set the mode control and enter a 1 in the "serial in for right shift" input D.
    f.   Clock this 1 entry to the right two or three times. Set the mode control for left shift and clock left twice. Record the results.
    g.   Enter a 1 on the shift left serial input. Shift it left two or three counts. Change the mode switch and shift the entry to the right out of the register. Record the events.

EXPERIMENT 8-2   RING COUNTER

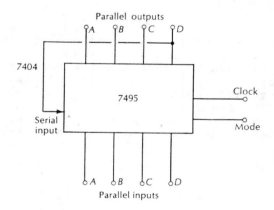

Figure 8-3 Ring Counter

The ring counter requires no decoding but the decoder display circuit will be left intact. The ring counter is a circulating shift register and can contain only a single 1 or a single 0 for an allowed counting sequence. If the counting sequence begins with a disallowed entry (two or more 0's combined with two or more 1's), the counter will count in a disallowed subroutine. These disallowed subroutines will be examined as well as the normal count routine.

OBJECTIVES:

    a.   To examine the normal count sequence for the shift register ring counter.
    b.   To examine the disallowed subroutines that are possible with the ring counter.
    c.   To test a method of eliminating disallowed subroutines.

MATERIALS:

    a.   A 7495 shift register
    b.   A 7404 hex inverter
    c.   A 7410 triple three-input NAND gate
    d.   Extra level switches as needed

EQUIPMENT:

    a.   Logic trainer

PROCEDURE:

Part I: The Normal Sequence

    a.   Connect the circuit as shown in Figure 8-3.
    b.   Connect level switches to A, B, C, D parallel inputs
        and to the mode control.
        Connect the two clock inputs together and connect
        them to a level switch.
    c.   Use the parallel input level switches to preset
        the counter to $Q_a = 1$, $Q_b = Q_c = Q_d = 0$.
    d.   Set mode to serial right shift and clock the
        counter through its complete sequence. Use 1
        pulse per second clock rate or clock it manually
        with the bounceless pushbutton. Complete the count
        sequence diagram in Figure 8-4.

no 7404 (handwritten)

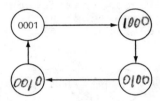

Figure 8-4 Count Sequence Diagram for the
Desired Counting Routine

Part II: Disallowed Conditions

    e.   Preload the register with the following states:

	2^3	2^2	2^1	2^0	
1.	0	0	0	0	*nothing lites*
2.	0	1	1	0	*ring count*
3.	1	1	1	0	*count*
4.	1	0	1	0	*count*
5.	1	1	1	1	*all lites*

    f.   Clock the counter through each sequence and plot
       each one on a diagram.

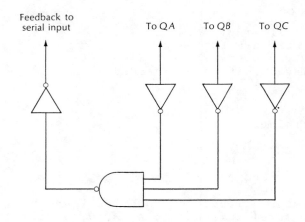

Feedback to serial input   To QA   To QB   To QC

Figure 8-5   Feedback Circuit for a Four-Flip-Flop Ring Counter
Provides Self-Starting and Self-Correction

Part III: Eliminating Disallowed Subroutines

    g.   Connect the gate circuit shown in Figure 8-5.
    h.   Preload each of the combinations in Part IIe.
         Clock the counter through until you are certain
         that the normal count sequence is occurring.
    i.   Draw a sequence diagram showing how the counter
         steps from a disallowed combination into the
         normal routine (see Figure 8-6).

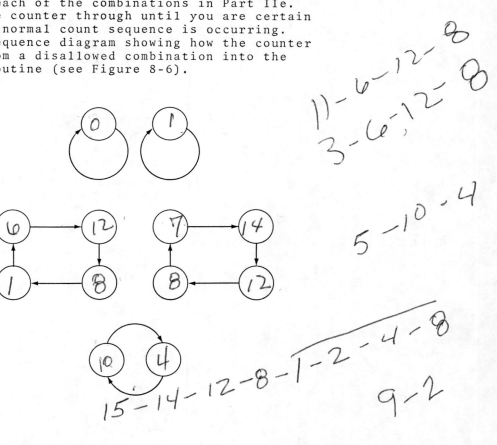

Figure 8-6   Sequence diagrams for Disallowed Subroutines

82

EXPERIMENT 8-3   THE JOHNSON COUNTER

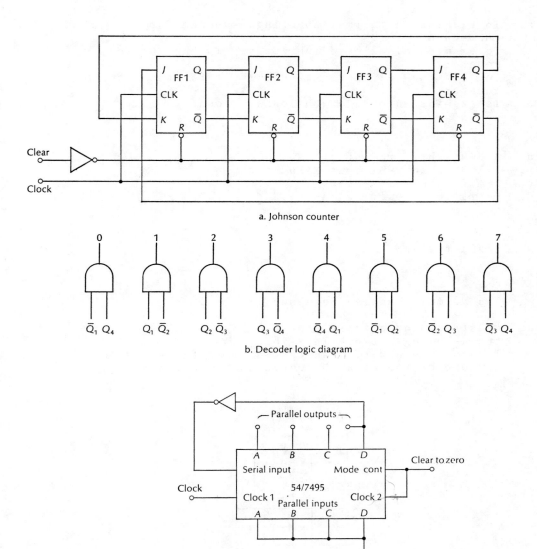

a. Johnson counter

b. Decoder logic diagram

c. Johnson Counter Implemented with the 7495 Shift Register

Figure 8-7   The Basic Johnson Counter

The Johnson counter requires decoding that is different from the normal decoding used with the common binary count sequence. The four-bit Johnson counter and the decoding network are shown in Figure 8-7.

OBJECTIVES:

    a. To examine the normal counting sequence for the Johnson counter.

    b. To examine disallowed subroutines in the Johnson counter.

    c. To test the self-correcting circuit for the Johnson counter.

    d. To examine an odd-length Johnson counter.

MATERIALS:

    a. A 7495 shift register
    b. A 7400 quad two-input NAND gate
    c. Two 7404 hex inverters
    d. Extra level switches as needed

EQUIPMENT:

    a. Logic trainer

PROCEDURE:

Part I: The Normal Counting Sequence

    a. Construct the circuit shown in Figure 8-7c including the decoding network in 8-7b.

    b. Turn on the power. Use the level switches and load any one of the allowed conditions (see Table 8-1).

State	Flip-flop			
	A	B	C	D
0	0	0	0	0
1	1	0	0	0
2	1	1	0	0
3	1	1	1	0
4	1	1	1	1
5	0	1	1	1
6	0	0	1	1
7	0	0	0	1
0	0	0	0	0

Table 8-1 Truth Table for the
Four F-F Johnson Counter

    c. Record the results.

Part II: Disallowed Subroutines

    d. Load 0100 into the shift register.

    e. Turn on the counter and make a sequence diagram of the disallowed subroutine.

f. The following are disallowed conditions:
    1101, 0110, 1011, 0101, 0010, 1001, 0100, 1010.
    Do any of these lead to a different disallowed sub-
    routine? You can find out experimentally.

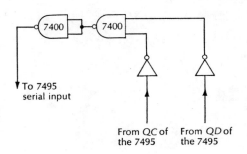

To 7495
serial input

From Q_C of
the 7495

From Q_D of
the 7495

Note: This network replaces the inverter in Figure 8-7c.

Figure 8-8   Johnson Counter Correction
Feedback Network

Part III: Eliminating the Disallowed Subroutine Problem

    g. Connect the correction network in Figure 8-8 to
        the counter.
    h. Load one of the disallowed conditions into the
        register and write a summary of the results.

Part IV: The Odd-Length Johnson Counter

    i. Remove the correction circuit from the counter.
    j. Move the input of the inverter (Figure 8-8)
        from Q_d to Q_c.
    k. Load the counter with 0000.
    l. Start the counter and make a sequence diagram.

CHAPTER NINE

ARITHMETIC CIRCUITS

EXPERIMENT 9-1   THE HALF ADDER, FULL ADDER, HALF
SUBTRACTER, AND FULL SUBTRACTER

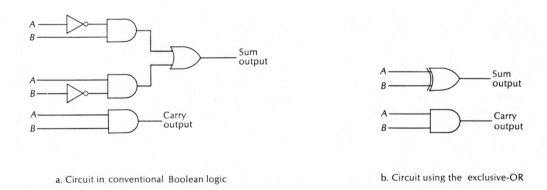

a. Circuit in conventional Boolean logic

b. Circuit using the exclusive-OR

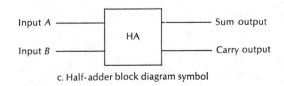

c. Half-adder block diagram symbol

Figure 9-1   Logic Circuit to Perform Binary Addition

The basis arithmetic circuit is the adder. The simplest adder is called the half adder. The addition of an inverter to the half adder converts it into a simple substraction circuit called a half subtracter. An exclusive-OR gate can be used as a conditional inverter that makes it possible to make the basic circuit function as a half adder or half subtracter by placing either a logical 1 or a logical 0 on a <u>mode</u> input (one of the X-OR inputs). Two half adder/subtracter circuits can be combined to form a full adder/subtracter.

OBJECTIVES:

    a.   To construct and evaluate the half adder and half subtracter.

    b.   To construct and evaluate the full adder and full subtracter.

MATERIALS:

    a.   A 7486 quad two-input X-OR gate

    b.   A 7432 quad two-input OR gate

EQUIPMENT:

    a.   Logic trainer

Adders and Subtractors: General Information

    1.   The Half Adder

        The binary addition rules for the addition of two bits can be summarized as follows:

$A + B =$	Sum	Carry
0 + 0 =	0	0
0 + 1 =	1	0
1 + 0 =	1	0
1 + 1 =	0	1

        The addition rules can be written in the form of truth tables and the logic developed from the tables.

    2.   The Sum Table

A	B	Sum	minterms
0	0	0	
0	1	1	$(\overline{A}\ B)$
1	0	1	$(A\ \overline{B})$
1	1	0	

        The sum equation is

        $\text{Sum} = \overline{A}\ B + A\ \overline{B}$

This is the exclusive-OR function and can be written as

Sum = $A \oplus B$

3. The Carry Truth Table

A	B	Carry	minterms
0	0	0	
0	1	0	
1	0	0	
1	1	1	$(A \cdot B)$

4. The Carry Equation is

    Carry = $A \cdot B$

5. Subtraction Rules

$A - B =$	Difference	Borrow
0 - 0 =	0	0
0 - 1 =	1	1
1 - 0 =	1	0
1 - 1 =	0	0

6. Subtraction Difference Truth Table

A	B	Difference	Borrow
0	0	0	
0	1	1	$\overline{A}\, B$
1	0	1	
1	1	0	

7. The Borrow Equation is

    $B = \overline{A} \cdot B$

8. Summary of Equations

    a. Addition

    Sum = $A \oplus B$

    Carry = $A \cdot B$

    b. Subtraction

    Difference = $A \oplus B$

    Carry = $\overline{A} \cdot B$

Figure 9-1 shows the complete half-adder circuit.

9. The Conditional Inverter and True Complement Generator

An exclusive-OR gate can be made to invert a logic level or pass it on in its true state. Figure 9-2 shows a conditional inverter and a four-bit true/complement generator. Figure 9-3 shows the half-subtractor circuit and combined half-adder/half-subtracter circuit.

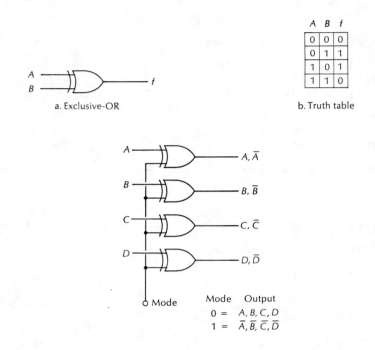

A	B	f
0	0	0
0	1	1
1	0	1
1	1	0

a. Exclusive-OR

b. Truth table

Mode	Output
0 =	A, B, C, D
1 =	$\bar{A}, \bar{B}, \bar{C}, \bar{D}$

c. Four-bit true/complement generator

Figure 9-2   True/Complement Generator

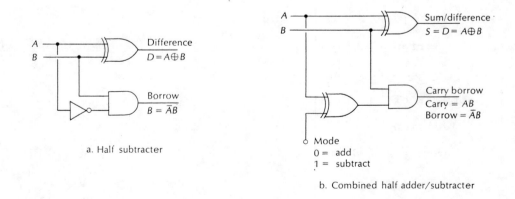

a. Half subtracter

b. Combined half adder/subtracter

Figure 9-3   Half Subtracter, Half Adder/
Subtracter and Full Subtracter

PROCEDURE:

   a. Connect the circuit as shown in Figure 9-3b.
   b. Connect the sum and carry outputs to indicator
      lamps on the trainer.
   c. Connect the inputs and <u>mode</u> control to level
      switches and indicator lamps.
   d. Set the <u>mode</u> control for addition and complete
      Table 9-1b.
   e. Set the mode control for subtraction and complete
      Table 9-2b.

$A + B$		Sum	Carry
0	0	0	0
0	1	1	0
1	0	1	0
1	1	0	1

a. Addition truth table

$A + B$		Sum	Carry
0	0		
0	1		
1	0		
1	1		

b. Experimental results

Table 9-1 Addition Truth Table

$A - B$		Difference	Borrow
0	0	0	0
0	1	1	1
1	0	1	0
1	1	0	0

a. Subtraction table

$A - B$		Difference	Borrow
0	0		
0	1		
1	0		
1	1		

b. Experimental results

Table 9-2 Subtraction Truth Table

Note: Leave the circuit connected for following
experiments.

10. The Full Adder/Subtracter

   A complete (full) adder must be capable of adding two bits plus
a carry from a preceding addition; thus it must have three inputs. A full
subtracter must subtract one bit from another as well as subtracting a
borrow when it is required. The full subtracter must also have three inputs. A full adder can be formed from two half adders, and a full subtracter can be formed from two half subtracters. Likewise, a full adder/sub-
tracter can be formed from two half adder/subtracters.

91

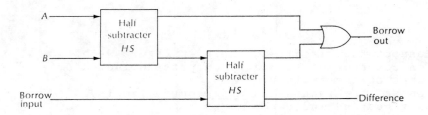

Figure 9-4 Two Half Subtracters Connected
as a Full Subtracter

PROCEDURE:

a. Construct a second half adder/subtracter.
b. Connect the one constructed earlier and the second one as shown in Figure 9-4.
c. Connect the two putputs to indicator lamps.
d. Connect the three inputs to level switches and indicator lamps (or decoder display circuits).
e. Connect the two <u>mode</u> controls together to a level switch.
f. Set the <u>mode</u> control to <u>add</u> and complete truth table 9-3b.
g. Set the <u>mode</u> control to <u>subtract</u> and complete truth table 9-4b.

A	B	C	Sum	Carry
0	0	0	0	0
0	0	1	1	0
0	1	0	1	0
0	1	1	0	1
1	0	0	1	0
1	0	1	0	1
1	1	0	0	1
1	1	1	1	1

a. The full adder table

A	B	C	Sum	Carry
0	0	0		
0	0	1		
0	1	0		
0	1	1		
1	0	0		
1	0	1		
1	1	0		
1	1	1		

b. Experimental results

Table 9-3 Full Adder

A	B	C	Difference	Borrow
0	0	0	0	0
0	0	1	1	1
0	1	0	1	1
0	1	1	0	1
1	0	0	1	0
1	0	1	1	0
1	1	0	0	0
1	1	1	1	1

a. Full subtractor table

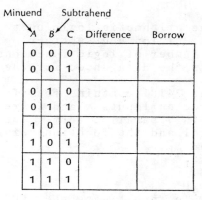

Minuend	Subtrahend			
A	B	C	Difference	Borrow
0	0	0		
0	0	1		
0	1	0		
0	1	1		
1	0	0		
1	0	1		
1	1	0		
1	1	1		

b. Experimental results

Table 9-4 Full Subtracter

EXPERIMENT 9-2   THE ARITHMETIC LOGIC UNIT (ALU)

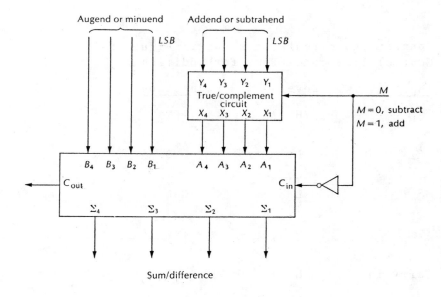

Figure 9-5 Two's Complement Adder/Subtracter

93

The arithmetic logic unit (ALU) is a parallel data-handling device with both addition and subtraction capabilities as well as the ability to provide a number of logic functions. The full capabilities of the ALU are detailed in the data sheet for the 74181.

The 74181 contains four full parallel adder/subtracter circuits. Data entered on inputs A and B are processed and the sum or difference is outputted in a parallel form. The mode of operation is controlled by the mode control and the function being performed is controlled by inputs S_0, S_1, S_2, and S_3.

OBJECTIVES:

      a. To investigate the ALU in the parallel addition mode.
      b. To investigate the ALU in the parallel subtraction (two's complement) mode.

MATERIALS:

      a. 74181 ALU
      b. Two decoder display circuits
      c. True/complement generator circuit from Figure 9-2
      d. A 7486 X-OR gate
      e. A 7404 hex inverter

EQUIPMENT:

      Logic trainer

PROCEDURE:

Addition

      a. Connect the circuit as shown in Figure 9-5.
      b. Control line conditions for addition:

Input	Level	Connection
S_3	H	+5V
S_2	L	GND
S_1	L	GND
S_0	H	+5V
Carry in	H	+5V
Mode	L	GND

      c. Connect input A and input B level switches to the addend/augend inputs.
      d. Connect the four output lines of the ALU to four indicator lamps.
      e. Set up at least two addition problems. Record input values, output indicator states, and the decimal equivalent of the output indicator lamps.

f. Verify that the ALU is performing binary addition in the form:

$$A_2 \qquad A_1 \qquad A_0$$

$$+ \; B_2 \qquad B_1 \qquad B_0$$

$$\text{Carry} \longrightarrow F_3 \quad F_2 \qquad F_1 \qquad F_0$$

Subtraction

g. Set the true/complement circuit mode control to subtract ($M=0$). Perform at least two subtractions and record your results.

PROBLEM:

The 74181 has internal provisions for two's complement subtraction. Using the manufacturer's data book, make a listing of control input settings for two's complement subtraction.

CHAPTER TEN

SEMICONDUCTOR MEMORIES

In the experiments that follow we will examine read/write (RAM) and read-only memories (ROM). In the experiment on RAM's we will use an off-the-shelf IC RAM, the 16-bit 7481A.

In the ROM experiment the ROM will be constructed from individual gates. This approach is taken to provide maximum learning flexibility. Commercial ROM packages are either factory-programmed or programmed by electrically burning open fusible links. In either case, the ROM, once programmed, cannot be altered. Erasable ROM's are available, but the relatively high cost of the devices and the ultraviolet light source required to erase them makes them somewhat impractical in a school laboratory situation.

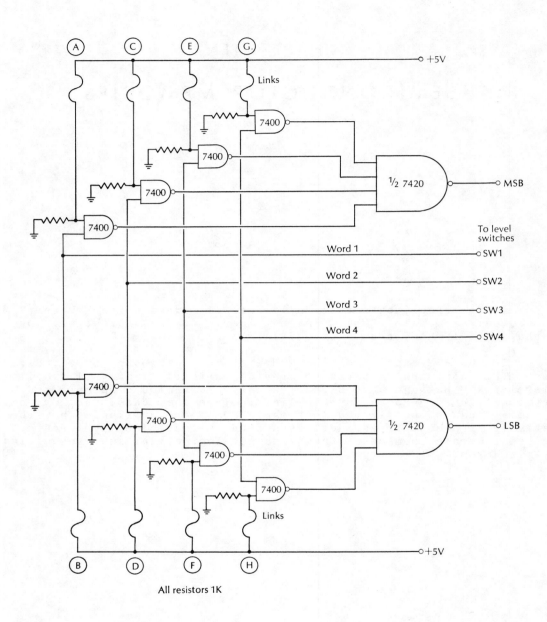

Figure 10-1 Logic Diagram for the Experimental ROM

OBJECTIVE:

    a.   To construct and test a two-bit by four-word ROM.

MATERIALS:

    a.   Two 7400 quad two-input NAND gates
    b.   A 7420 dual four-input NAND gate
    c.   Eight resistors 1KΩ

EQUIPMENT:

    a.   Logic trainer

SW1 Word 1	SW2 Word 2	SW3 Word 3	SW4 Word 4	Output
1	0	0	0	_____
0	1	0	0	_____
0	0	1	0	_____
0	0	0	1	_____

Table 10-1   ROM Program Table

PROCEDURE:

    a.   Connect the circuit as shown in Figure 10-1. The links can be slide switches, wire links, or whatever method you might come up with.
    b.   Program the memory by opening appropriate links. Record the data you have programmed on Table 10-1.
    c.   Switch all word switches to GND. Switch word switch SW1 to <u>high</u>. Record the output result on Table 10-2. Return $\overline{SW1}$ to <u>low</u>. Repeat for SW2, SW3, and SW4.

Word 1	Word 2	Word 3	Word 4	Output
1	0	0	0	_____
0	1	0	0	_____
0	0	1	0	_____
0	0	0	1	_____

Table 10-2   ROM Word Output Table

PROBLEM:

    a.   What happens if two or more word switches are <u>high</u> at the same time?

_____

_____

_____

EXPERIMENT 10-2   THE READ/WRITE (RAM) MEMORY

OBJECTIVE:

   a. To become familiar with the connections and
      operating characteristics of an IC static RAM.

MATERIALS:

   a. A 7481A sixteen-bit bipolar RAM
   b. Extra level switches as required

EQUIPMENT:

   a. Logic trainer

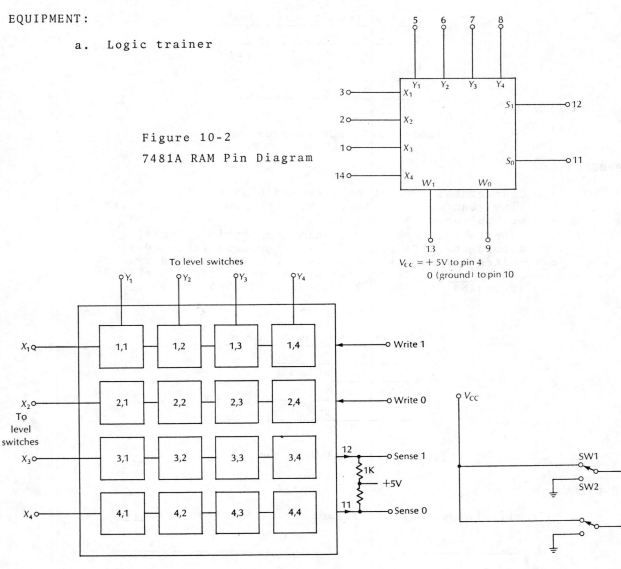

Figure 10-2

7481A RAM Pin Diagram

V_{CC} = + 5V to pin 4
0 (ground) to pin 10

a. RAM circuit

b. Level switch connections

Figure 10-3   RAM Circuit

100

PROCEDURE:

    a.   Figure 10-2 shows the pin diagram for the 7481A sixteen-bit RAM. Figure 10-3 shows the experimental circuit for the experiment along with cell designations and load resistors for the open collector sense amplifiers. Connect the circuit as shown in Figure 10-3. Connect pins 11 and 12 to indicator lamps on the trainer.

To operate the memory:

    b.   Connect all X and Y select lines and both write inputs to GND. <u>Clear</u> all <u>locations</u>.

    c.   To select a bit, switch the appropriate X and Y lines to +5 volts.

    d.   To write a 1 into the selected bit, move the write 1 switch to +5 and return it to GND. This will make the S_0 output (pin 11) <u>high</u> and the S_1 (pin 12) <u>low</u>.

    e.   To write a 0 into the selected bit, move the write 0 switch to +5 and return it to GND. This will make the S_0 output (pin 11) <u>low</u> and the S_1 output (pin 12) <u>high</u>.

    f.   To read previously stored information, select a bit as in step c and observe the indicator lamps.

    g.   Write a set of data of your choice into the memory. Record what you have written on Table 10-3, column A.

    h.   Read the stored data out of the memory and record the results on Table 10-3, column B.

    i.   To determine if the data was destroyed in the reading, cycle through the memory contents and record the results on Table 10-3, column C.

    j.   To test for volatility, turn off the power and then restore it. Read out the memory contents again and record the results on Table 10-3, column D.

Cell Location	Part A	B	C	D
1,1				
1,2				
1,3				
1,4				
2,1				
2,2				
2,3				
2,4				
3,1				
3,2				
3,3				
3,4				
4,1				
4,2				
4,3				
4,4				

Table 10-3   RAM Truth Table

Cell Location	Part			
	A	B	C	D
1,1				
1,2				
1,3				
1,4				
2,1				
2,2				
2,3				
2,4				
3,1				
3,2				
3,3				
3,4				
4,1				
4,2				
4,3				
4,4				

Table 10-4   RAM Truth Table

PROBLEMS:

a. Is the data altered in the reading process?

_____

In what way? _____

_____

_____

b. Is the data lost as a result of power shutdown?

_____

c. Is the memory considered to be volatile?

_____

d. Is the memory destructive readout (DRO) or non--
destructive readout (NDRO)?

_____

CHAPTER ELEVEN

INTERFACING

EXPERIMENT 11-1   DECADE COUNTER USING 8T70 SERIES INTERFACE

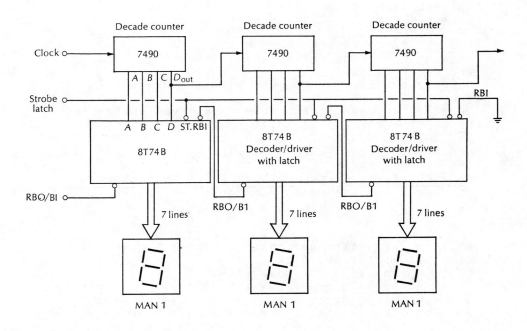

Figure 11-1   Counter Circuit Using Decoder/Driver/
Latch Interface Unit

OBJECTIVES:

    a. To construct and evaluate a three-decade counter.
    b. To see how leading 0 blanking operates.
    c. To observe the action of a storage latch in a counting system.

MATERIALS:

    a. Three 7490 decade and three 7493 binary counters
    b. Three 8T74B, BCD-to-seven-segment decoder/drivers with latch
    c. Three Man 1 or equivalent common anode seven-segment readout units.

Note: With the 8T74 decoder no series limiting resistors are required for the LED's.

EQUIPMENT:

    a. Logic trainer

PROCEDURE:

    a. Connect the circuit as shown in Figure 11-1 using 7490 counters.
    b. Connect the counter clear inputs to a level switch.
    c. Connect the latch strobe line to a level switch.
    d. Connect RBI on the rightmost decoder to a level switch.
    e. Put data strobe latch line level switch to ground.
    f. Connect RBO/BI of the leftmost decoder to a level switch. This input can be used for blanking. Caution: This input most not be forced <u>high</u> when RBI AND A B C D are all low. This can cause device damage. For now, set to <u>high</u>.

    g. Put RBI level switch to ground.
    h. Turn on the power, clear the counter and start the clock signal.
    i. Observe the display to make sure the circuit is functioning.
    j. To store a count, take the strobe level switch to <u>high</u>. The counter is still counting, but the $\overline{\text{latch}}$ is holding the previous count.
    k. Restart the count display action by taking the latch line low.
    l. Move RBI level switch to high. Set the latch. Try latching and counting several times.

PROBLEMS:

    a. What is the difference in the display presentation with RBI at <u>low</u> and <u>high</u>?
    b. What happens if BI is taken low? Replace the 7490 counters with 7493 binary counters and repeat the experiment. Make a sketch of LED segments for counts beyond 9 (in any decade).

c. What <u>word</u> is hidden in this count? Do you need any?

_____

_____

SPECIAL CHALLENGE PROBLEMS:

    a. Devise a power-line-derived, one-second time base
        for the counter in Figure 11-1.
    b. Devise a control circuit to count for one second,
        and display for approximately ten seconds.
        Arrange to hold the latch during counting to
        eliminate flickering of display during counting.
    c. Use the counter system to measure frequency (use
        decade counters).

APPENDIX I

LOGIC TRAINERS

BREADBOARD SOCKETS

     Sockets should be able to accommodate at least eight 16-pin IC's. These are available from the following suppliers:

> AP Products, Inc.
> Box 110-R
> Plainsville, Ohio 44077
> Model 264L
>
> Continental Specialties Corp.
> 44 Kendall St., Box 1942
> New Haven, Ct. 06509

PARTS LIST

Power Supply

TI	Transformer 24V center tapped triad 45-X or equivalent
Regulator	National LM209K or Motorola MLM209K in a TO-3 package mounted on heat sink
D_1, D_2	Silicon diode 100-600V 1 amp to 3 amp
C_1	$330\mu F$ electrolytic, 50V
C_2	$0.1\mu F$ disc capacitor

Hex Lamp Driver

    LED   6 LED's
    Resistors   330
    7406   hex inverter driver

Debounced Pushbutton Circuit

    7400   Quad two-input NAND gate
                Spring-loaded SPDT pushbutton
                Resistors (2) 2.2 K

Clock Circuit

    7403   Quad NAND (open collector), or
    7405   Hex inverter (open collector)

Resistors (3) 2.2 K

    C_1 33 μFD   6.3V electrolytic

    C_2 3.3 μFD   6.3V electrolytic

    C_3 .33 μFD   12V   disc, ceramic

    C_4 .03 μFD   50V   disc, ceramic

    C_5 .003 μFD   50V   disc, ceramic

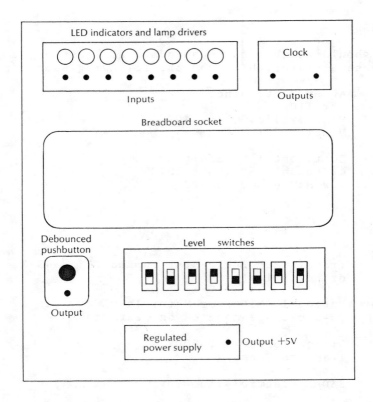

Figure 1   Logic Trainer Layout

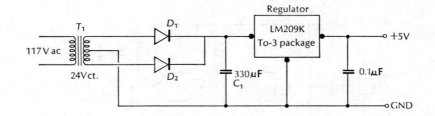

Figure 2   Logic Trainer Power Supply

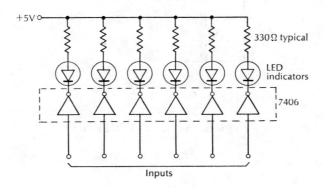

Figure 3   Hex Lamp Driver

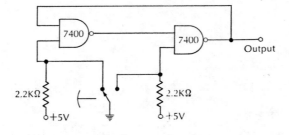

Figure 4   Debounced Pushbutton

109

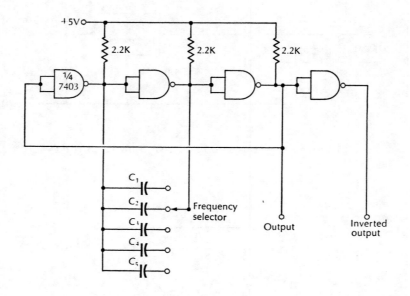

Figure 5   Clock Circuit

APPENDIX II

INTEGRATED CIRCUIT
BASING DIAGRAMS

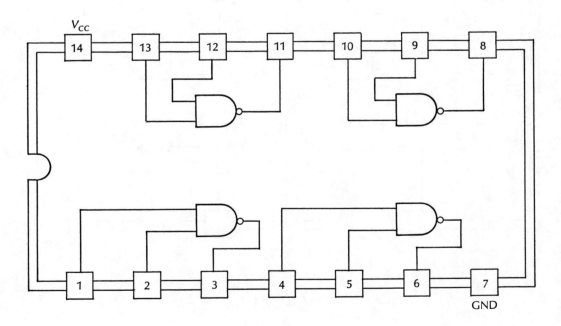

Figure 1   7400

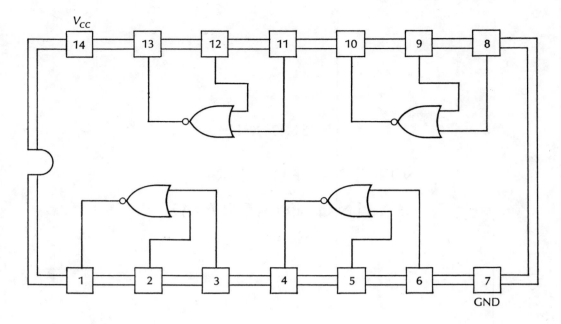

Figure 2   7402

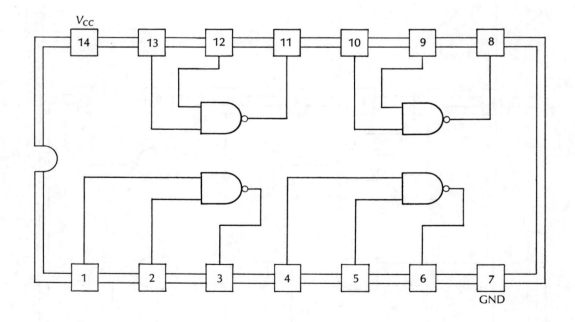

Figure 3   7403 (Open Collector)

112

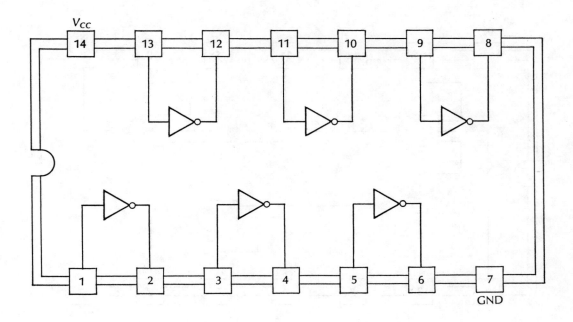

Figure 4   7404

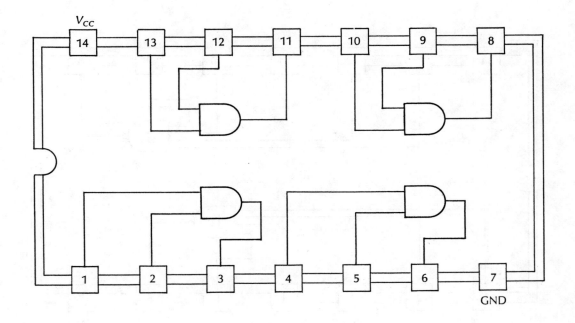

Figure 5   7408

113

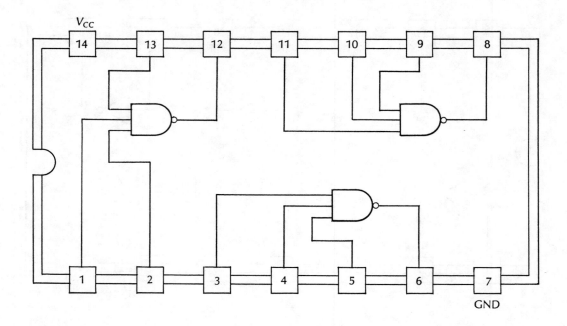

Figure 6   7410

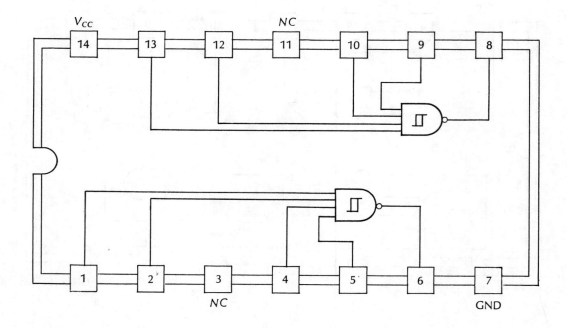

Figure 7   7413

114

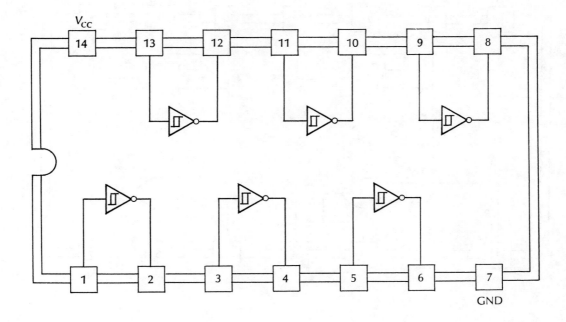

Figure 8   7414

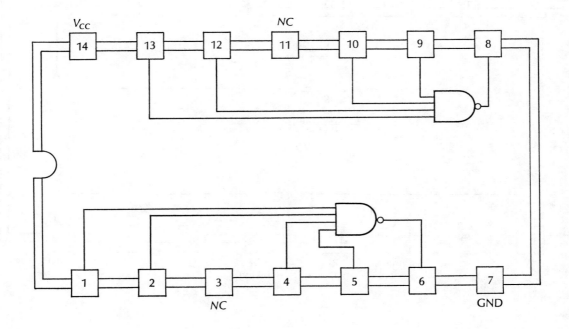

Figure 9   7420

115

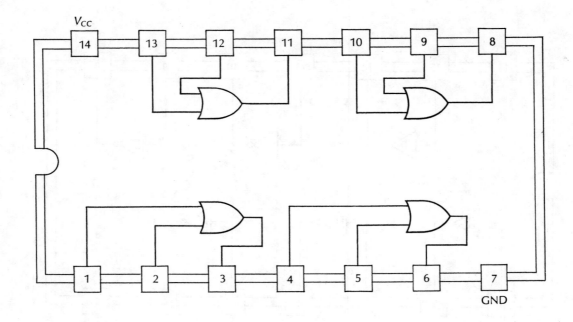

Figure 10   7432

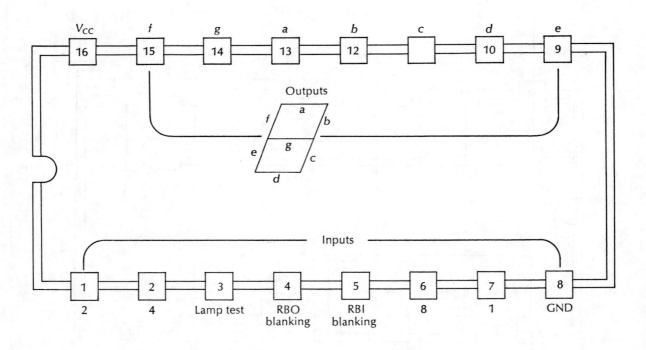

Figure 11   7447 BCD to Seven-Segment Decoder

116

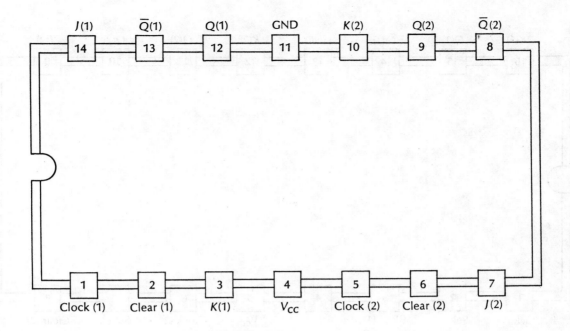

Figure 12   7473 Dual J-K Flip-Flop (with preclear only)

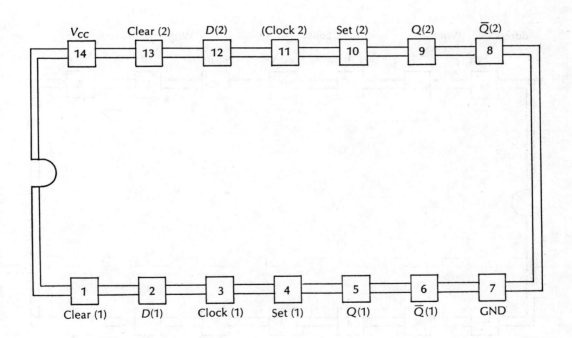

Figure 13   7474 Dual "D" Edge-Triggered Flip-Flop
(with preset and preclear)

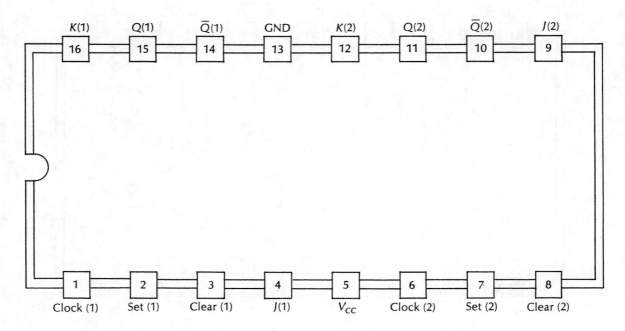

Figure 14   7476 Dual J-K Flip-Flop (with preset
and preclear, level-triggered)

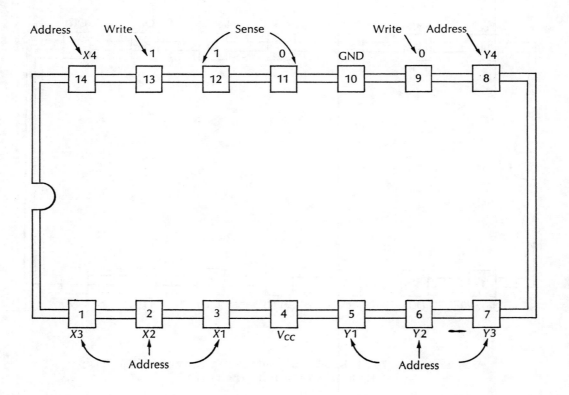

Figure 15   7481A (7484A) Bipolar Memory

118

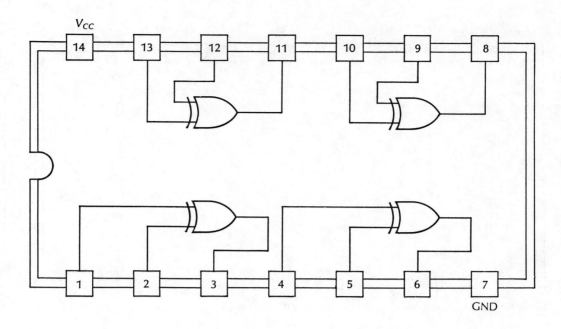

Figure 16   7486 Quad Exclusive-OR

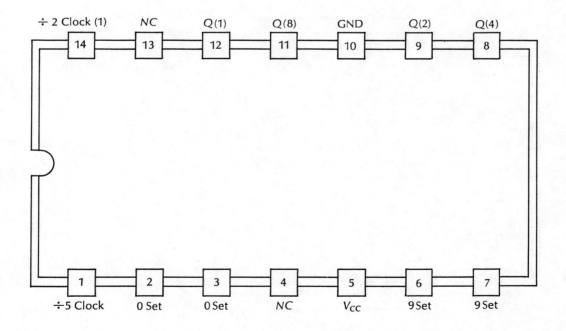

Figure 17   7490 Decade Counter

119

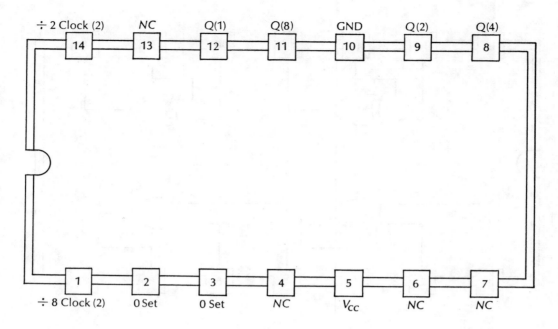

Figure 18   7493 Binary Counter

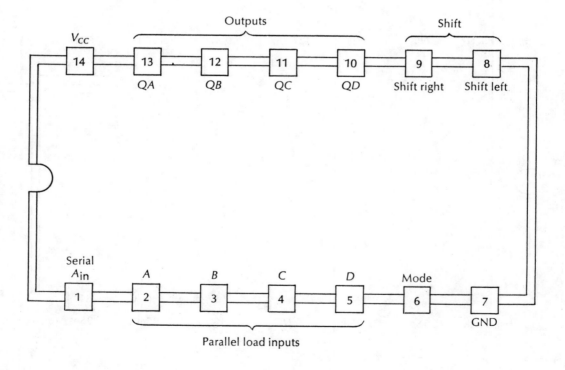

Figure 19   7495 Shift Register

120

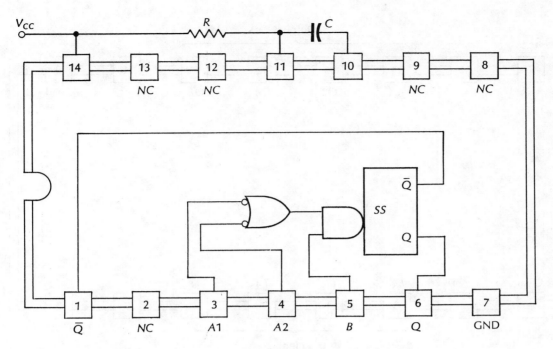

Figure 20   74121 Monostable Multivibrator

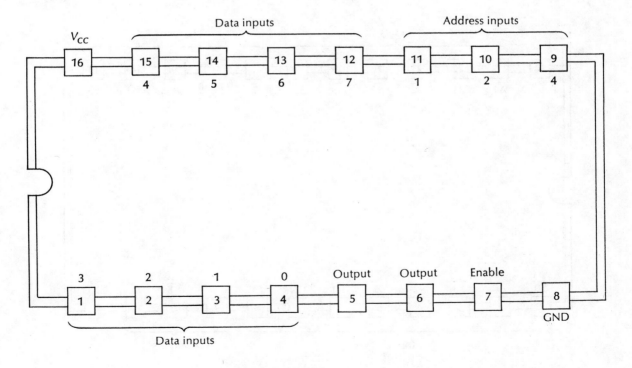

Figure 21   74151 Data Selector

121

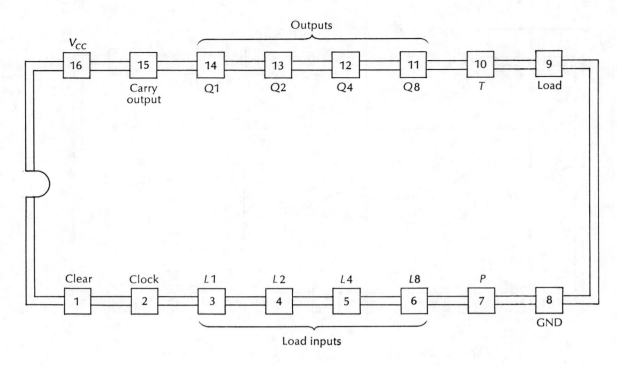

Figure 22   74161 Presettable Counter

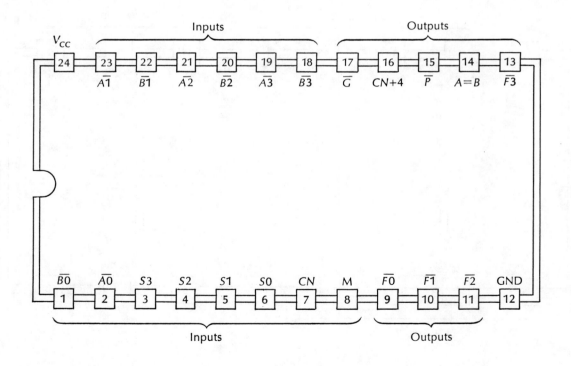

Figure 23   74181 Arithmetic/Logic Unit (ALU)

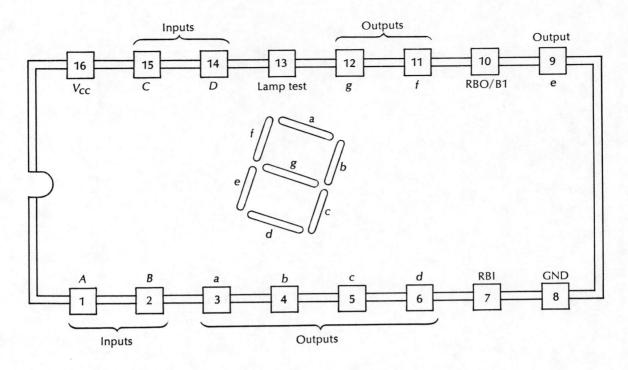

Figure 24   8T04 (05,06) BCD to Seven-Segment
Decoder Driver

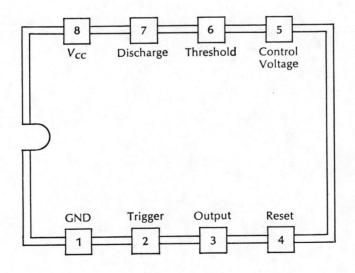

Figure 25   555 Timer

APPENDIX III

DIGITAL TECHNOLOGY
NOTEBOOK

On the following two pages you will find a sample title and entry page for a loose-leaf laboratory notebook.

The sample entry page shows you what a typical page looks like. For more information on guidelines for laboratory reporting reread the Introduction to this manual.

DIGITAL TECHNOLOGY

NOTEBOOK

NAME: _____

COURSE: _____

EXPERIMENT NO._____ NAME:_____

TITLE: _____ Date:_____ Course:_____

_____ Instructor:_____

Page: ____ of ____ pages

Signature:_____

Witness: Date:

1. _____

2. _____